Like In The Hidden Days? * The Monkey With The Funny Coloured Bum * God's Spy Do * Mam's Thighs * Two Wheelers, Inf
wn Voice' * The Tooth Fairy * Split The Kipper * Taking The Plaster Off * Hiccups * Good Mood Or B
alls * Volume 03 'In Their Own Backyard' * Empty Bottles * Bent Ci           Po
-ups & An' All That * Volume 04 'In Their Own Front Par              As
Settee Secrets * This Sporting Life * Parlour Games * Volume            ber
In Their Own Back Ole' * Humpty Dumpty * Penny Black          ay
nette' * The Mind Boggles * School Baths * Tread Carefully               Na
e 08 'In Their Own Belly Tub' * Early Birds * Horse S              Mo
Over The Top * Volume 09 'In Their Own Thingy'            chts
ht * Guessing Games * Different Worlds * Volume 10 'In Their Own Firelight' * Wash Carts
Man's All Heart * Who's For Pudding? * Nuts & Razors * A Little Bit Of Privateness * Volume     n
Their Own String Vest' * Jumble Sale * Blowing Your Own Trumpet * Embrocation Wrong Location * Just For
* Motor Biking * Is It Catching? * Upstairs Downstairs * Wind & Witches * Birthday Boy * Getting Up Y
he Rack * Volume 14 'In Their Own Footsteps' * Stranded Alf * Fleabag * Affable Alf & Dra
utting Corners * Twenty Questions * Eye To Eye * Rubadub Alf * Volume 15 'In Their Own Pigeon
ume 16 'In Their Own Ebb & Flow' * Tea & Sympathy * Legless Tommy * Pawnshop Saga * C
Class' * Tin Hats & Hard Times * Crash Diet * Benevolent Alf * Departure Day * On The Pr
es Too Big * Back To School * Blue Alf & Cardinal Red * Volume 18 'In Their Own Woolly Jumper'
g Their Business * The Party's Over * Volume 19 'In Their Own Cobbled Street' * Rice & Dobbers * Porky Pies & Highla
Firm Hand * Volume 20 'In Their Own Flat Cap' * Artistic Temperature * Sugar & Spice * Only
* Out Of Tune * Upright & Bendy * The Lost Chord * Awkward Questions * Tiggy Off The Ground * The Stra
eir Own Wellybobs' * Happy Days * All Ears * Stick-on Soles * Merrylegs & The Brewcan * The G
ng * Volume 23 'In Their Own Knitted Trunks' * A Little Misunderstanding * Sir Billy * Balloons & Newts
nes & Fishing Nets * Getting The Point * Volume 24 'In Their Own Daze' * Rude Awakening * Conkers & T
ad Freddie & The Dentists * Dimp Picking * Not Far Now * All Over Nowt * Volume 25 'In Their Own Owzyerfa
* Mam's Thighs * Two Wheelers, Influence & Wee * Ragbone & Dad's Brown Mac * Marbles * Fixing The Window * Bonfire Night
* Hiccups * Good Mood Or Bad Mad * The Runaway * Wot's Yer Belly Button For? * The Old Tin Bath
Bent Cigs & Corndog * Politics & Beans * The Clubman Cometh * Tea-Time * Whit Walks
Vimto Lollies * As Alf As A Newt * Sleeping Out * Lying In * A Mouse's Tale * Family Album
heir Own Time' * Lumber In Slumber * Liver & Honions * Audrey Tries Her Luck * Postman's Knoc
nny Arrow Bars * Don't Say Circus * Piling On The Agony * When Playing Out Was In * Little Lodgers
tly Speaking * Sunday Names * We Know What You're Doing * Female Logic * Give Them A Wa
* Being A Darer * All Mod Cons * Wet Kecks & Aniseed Balls * Taters * A Round Meal
ng Chicken * Rudiments * Auntie Pamela's Jumper * A Helping Hand * The Posh Cat
Firelight' * Wash Carts & Hand Carts * God Bothering * Pitch Black * Folies Backyard
s * Volume    In Their Own Daze'    * Zippa Dee Doodah * A Chip Off The Old Block * Down To The Wood
ation Wrong Location * Just For Luck * Bye Bye Tater Pie * Gobstopping * No More No Thanks * One On One Off
* Birthday Boy * Getting Up Yer Nose * A Latch Lifter * Cardboard Feet & Providence * Baths & Aftermaths
Fleabag * Affable Alf & Draughts * Ooh Men! * Saturday Matinee * Chicken's Feet & Alf's Hands
e 15 'In Their Own Pigeon 'Ole' * Cock O'The Class * Other Dads * Bingo Night * Return Of The Mouse
ommy * Pawnshop Saga * Checkmate * No Rest For The Wicked * Bob-A-Job * Show Up Show Down
Departure Day * On The Prom * Home At Last * Cabbage & Ribs & Oil Cloths * Too Many Cook
heir Own Woolly Jumper' * Hamerica * Waterworks * Hammered Nails * The Wrigleys * Keep A Secret
ice & Dobbers * Porky Pies & Highland Flings * Goofy Giblin * Fathers Day & Crafty Alf * Grinders, Moodies & Ostriches
ture * Sugar & Spice * Only Joking * Canteen Santa * Apple Pie Custard Tins * The Visitor Fleas
ggy Off The Ground * The Strains of Tea * Bogeys & Custard * Nine Into Six Doesn't Go * Wet & Windy
ylegs & The Brewcan * The Great Debate * Spanish Magic * No Hiding Place * Surprise Surprise!
* Sir Billy * Balloons & Newts * A Minor Eruption * Rubbing It In * French With Tears * Fun In The Tunnel
Rude Awakening * Conkers & Toast * Something To Look Forward To * Alf Splashes Out * Roughing It A Bit

# BOOK

*YOU JUST COULDN'T MAKE IT UP!*

# OTHER PARAPHERNALIA

## BRADSHAWS AUDIO

*Vol 01 In Their Own Words*
*Vol 02 In Their Own Voice*
*Vol 03 In Their Own Backyard*
*Vol 04 In Their Own Front Parlour*
*Vol 05 In Their Own Time*
*Vol 06 In Their Own Door 'Ole*
*Vol 07 In Their Own Kitchenette*
*Vol 08 In Their Own Dolly Tub*
*Vol 09 In Their Own Thingy*
*Vol 10 In Their Own Firelight*
*Vol 11 In Their Own Opinion*
*Vol 12 In Their Own String Vest*
*Vol 13 In Their Own Lucky Bag*
*Vol 14 In Their Own Footsteps*
*Vol 15 In Their Own Pigeon 'Ole*
*Vol 16 In Their Own Ebb & Flow*
*Vol 17 In Their Own Class*
*Vol 18 In Their Own Woolley Jumper*
*Vol 19 In Their Own Cobbled Street*
*Vol 20 In Their Own Flat Cap*
*Vol 21 In Their Own Darned Socks*
*Vol 22 In Their Own Knitted Trunks*
*Vol 23 In Their Own Wellybobs*
*Vol 24 In Their Own Daze*
*Vol 25 In Their Own Owzyerfather*

COMPILATIONS...
*A Taste Of The Bradshaws*
*A Taste Of The Bradshaws 2*

COMING SOON...
*The Bradshaws Novel "Goosed"*
*Billy Bradshaw's Dead Good Hadventures*

## BUZZ HAWKINS AUDIO

*Catchy Choruses & Daft Bits*
*You Know Who You Are*

All CDs available online from the Bradshaws Corner Shop
www.thebradshaws.biz
All tracks available as downloads from iTunes and others

WRITTEN & CREATED BY

A 2upToons
Publication

Welcome to The Bradshaws An' All That. Filled to bursting with daft bits, did-they-really-do-that bits, ooh-you-can't-say-that bits, and bits from that nearly-gone era of all our yesterdays when your world was full of wonder and your mouth probably full of gobstoppers. Nostalgia really is what it used to be! Welcome to the world of of Billy, Alf and Audrey…
The Bradshaws!

# A BIT ABOUT THIS BOOK…

A LONG YET NOT-SO-LONG TIME AGO THE FOLLOWING WAS TRUE … MACS KEPT THE RAIN OFF YOU; PCS CAUGHT BURGLARS; GOOGLING WAS A SNEAKY WAY TO BOWL A CRICKET BALL; PODCASTING WAS HOW SOME VEGANS BAITED THEIR FISHING HOOKS WITH PEAS INSTEAD OF MAGGOTS; TWITTERING WAS WHAT YOUR BUDGIE DID WHEN YOU DIDN'T COVER THE CAGE UP; LOL WAS 3/5THS OF A LOLLY; AND A SMART PHONE WAS MUCH LIKE ANY OTHER PHONE – ATTACHED BY A CURLY WIRE TO A BULKY BAKELITE BASE WITH A BIG DIAL ON THE FRONT. IT WAS ONLY SMART IF YOUR MAM KEPT IT CLEAN AND POLISHED, BUT ANYWAY, MOST OF US KEPT OUR PHONES IN THE KIOSK.

THE BRADSHAWS AN' ALL THAT IS WRITTEN ESPECIALLY FOR P.G. KIDS[1] AND CHILDISH GROWN-UPS AND THOSE OF US DAFT ENOUGH TO WANT TO MAKE A PAPER AEROPLANE OR FLY A KITE OR RIDE A WOODEN BOGEY OR PLAY FARMER-FARMER OR DO A HANDSTAND AGAINST THE WALL.

WE ALL HAVE TO GROW OLDER BUT WE DON'T HAVE TO GROW UP. HAVE FUN!

BUZZ HAWKINS

## GLOSSARY OF TERMS AND PRONUNCIATIONS
(for the benefit of unlocal readers)

Generally words which dictionarily begin with the letter aitch (h) - e.g. he, him, hat, house, hippococtypus - will ordinarlily (i.e. in Bradshaw-speak) begin with an apostrophe(')… the aitch being silent as in "banana".

"Accident" and its derivatives, in Billy-speak only, borrow a redundant aitch and become "haccident" ("haccidenkally-on-purpose", etc.). But then again they might not.

Tee or tees (t or tt) receive special ordinaryisating in Bradshaw-speak: e.g. - the tee (t) in getoff becomes double ar (rr)… gerroff. Another e.g. - specifically in Billy-speak, the tee (t) or tees (tt) in metal or bottle become cee-kay (ck)… meckle or bockle. One more e.g. - in Billy-speak only, tee-aitch (th) at the beginnings of words become eff (f)…
thing = fing, think = fink, thirty = firty etc.
MISCELLANEOUSLY…
t'int = it is not
boook/loook = book/look
wunt = would not
dunt = does not
scrike = cry
tek = take
'em = them
(Author's note…
I know this all sounds a bit confused and mixed up but I'm not untyping it now. Please don't read the above!)

[1] Parentally Guided kids.
(Please be aware: Alf Bradshaw is a ballbarian!)

# CONTENTS

# THE BRADSHAWS WHO ARE THEY?

## AUDREY BRADSHAW

Audrey is Billy's mam and is therefore older than him. She is also Alf's wife and is therefore younger than him. She firmly believes that women's brains are for other things far more interesting than thinking. She isn't fat and says that big legs run in her family. She makes upside down custard pies, unintentionally. She would really like a new Ewbank floor sweeper.

## BILLY BRADSHAW

Billy is 7-nearly-8. He wants a pet (a budgie would be best). He wants to be a zoo-keeper or sweet shop owner or racing car driver, depending on what day it is. He wants Winifred Dutton to stop trying to kiss him. He wants chips with everything. He can only skip on one foot (cos he's a boy), and he was born at home so he could be near his mother.

## ALF BRADSHAW

Alf is Audrey's husband and Billy's dad and is, by rights, head of the family – but only when he is allowed. He is male and therefore sadly, grotesquely, misunderstood. He never puts coal on the fire. He is, according to Audrey, an MCP – Male Shoulderless Pig. He firmly believes that a woman's brain is nearly as big as a human being's. His favourite sayings are 'Brew up, Audrey' and 'Bugger off!'

## FLEABAG THE CAT

Fleabag is the local tom cat who spends most of his time sitting on Alf's outside lav roof, licking it's nethers (cos it can). It must be a bit of a contortionist as it somehow manages to slip through the gap under the coal shed door and leave presents for Alf. Alf and Fleabag have an ongoing feud.

## MICHAEL MORRIS

Michael is Billy's best friend, except when he won't give Billy his bubbly gum back what Billy lent him. He wears clinic glasses with a patch over one eye. The other skens into the corner. He blows bubbles with his nose. He looks uncannily like the coalman. His mother, Betty, 'puts it about a bit' (says Alf).

## JOE WOODS

Alf's drinking pal. Nuff said.

## ADA WOODS

Ada is Audrey's Bingo pal and, like Audrey, understands men, having put up with her Joe for years. Alf says she should eat less pies and use the money to pay for the chair she broke

## NORMAN HINCHCLIFFE

Norman is very tall and Alf says he must have horse muck in his wellies. He has seven brothers and his father was some soldiers, or a giraffe (according to Alf). He is Billy's horse when they play cowboys and injuns.

## WINIFRED DUTTON

Winifred is in the Budgie gang cos she lives at the cake shop. She is always trying to stick the lips on Billy. Audrey thinks she's nice. Alf says she's a manipulating female.

AHHH !

And, of course, there's Uncle Wally One-ball (the one with the war wound, drags his leg), Fr Fanakerpan, Mr Bonsall, Betty Morris, the three-legged dog, and many more.

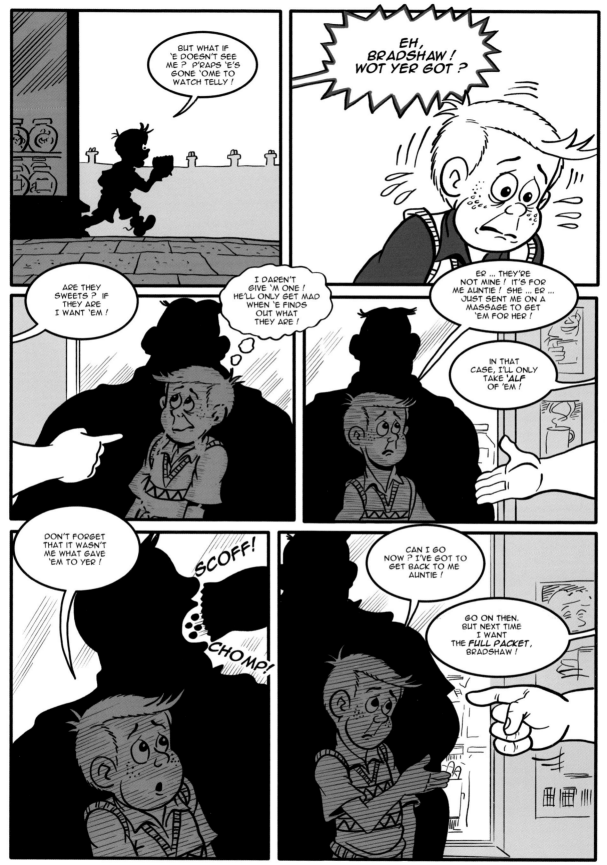

THE END

# TENUOUS LINK (LAXATIVES)

Speaking of laxatives ...
Gipsy Agnes Wobblybottom (Tea Leaf Reader, Clothes Peg Vendor, Tall Dark Handsome Man Dating Service Proprietor, available for consultations of a lifestyle and dietary nature) offers the following advice:

"Go easy with the cheese and eggs luv, and eat more cabbage to put a road through you. Then you might not need the laxatives."

Gipsy Agnes Wobblybottom (real name Doris Buttox) often does readings round at her house for Audrey Bradshaw and the girls from the wash-house and she comes highly recommended. Once, or so I'm told, she forecast that it would either rain or go dark before before morning. And it did. So look out for more lifestyle tips from Gipsy Agnes on her infamous "Your Life And Luck" horoscope pages somewhere else in this book (Don't ask me wherethey are, just have a gawp).

Meanwhile, just for fun, I've knocked up this odd little picture (below) made up of various popular laxatives (or unpopular, depending on your perpective). It's probably the first picture puzzle ever contrived of the names of laxatives and purgatives so, before you start whinging about my poor taste in subject matter, think yourself lucky that isn't made up of images of the actual effects of a damn good dose of 'em. By the way, don't go trying to memorise all these names because you'll probably find yourself reading the ingredients list on all your favourite foods, just in case. I do.

Anyway, see how many can you spot. Answers on a knitted toilet roll cover, please. Prize? The same as I got you last year.

*Answers on the following page*

ANSWERS TO THE LAXATIVES PUZZLE
(Contain yourself!)

BILE BEANS, EXLAX, MANNA, TAPAMINDS,
CASTOR OIL, SULPHUR, PETROLEUM,
MAGNESIA, SENNA, RHUBARB, JALAP,
COLOCYNTH, BUCKTHORN, ALOES,
CREAM OF TARTAR, SCAMMONY,
CALOMEL, EPSOM SALTS, GLAUBER'S
SALTS, SULPHATE OF POTASH, VENICE
TURPENTINE, FEAR.
21 LAXATIVES (22 if you count FEAR)

**S**peaking of chocolate - oh yes we were! One of the previously mentioned remedies - *EXLAX* it was - came in the form of a chocolate bar and that allows me yet another tenuous link.

Just look at this yummy picture of some of the chocolates and sweeties from way back. You might've just been able to afford some of them out of your spends or paper-round money. You can see how some of the wrapper designs changed (and the contents probably got smaller too) as they went through the 50's, 60's, 70, and 80's.

Anyway, there are more than enough here to get your mouth watering.

OOH, HOW TEMPTING IS THIS LOT?!

FRIENDLY HEALTH WARNING
TRY TO RESIST GOING TO MR BONSALL'S SWEET SHOP

Speaking of quizzes...
(Oh yes we were!)

## Once upon a time

There was no internet, no computer, no xbox or playstation, no mp3 player, and no 'I'm bored!' kids - unless it rained, that is, and they had to stay in and 'play nice'.

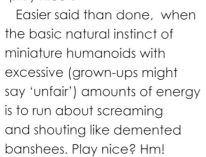

Easier said than done, when the basic natural instinct of miniature humanoids with excessive (grown-ups might say 'unfair') amounts of energy is to run about screaming and shouting like demented banshees. Play nice? Hm!

There's no arguing, it's a changed world. Back then, neighbours knew one another. *What?* Incredible but true. It was said that you could leave your doors open during the day. Maybe, but who'd want to steal a mangle? The streets were freedom - at least until that dreaded time, usually right in the middle of a game, when all the mothers came out on to the doorsteps and sang childrens' names in shrieky voices, and kids stopped playing while they tried to recognise their own moniker as it bounced off the rooftops. And when they did, they whinged - from a safe distance -

'Aw mam, it isn't even dark yet!'

Hopscotch, marbles, farmer-farmer, rope on a lamppost, two balls on the wall, kites made from newspaper, may I, truth-dare-kiss-command-or-promise, and the great favourite knock and run, were just a few of the games that kept kids out and parents sane. That was a time when *staying in* was definitely *out*.

I've crammed loads of great street games in this book. They're far too much fun to be wasted on kids so it's my hope that childish grown-ups will join in too! Just look out for the 'WHEN PLAYING OUT WAS IN' features.

And if the rain stopped kids from playing out (and it had to be near monsoon rain to do that) there was a feast of things for them to do indoors which, importantly, cost next to nowt. Of course, kids being kids, I can't guarantee they'll 'play nice' but I'm pretty sure they'll play happily. So in case the great British weather mucks things up (and that's distinctly possible),I've come up with lots of things to do indoors. Check out the 'HOW TO MAKE YOUR MEASLY SPENDS STRETCH EVEN MORE FURTHERER' pages (the title was Billy's idea). But first up, *Marbles*.

# LET'S DO OUR BIT FOR CONSERVATION – BY REVIVING STREET GAMES!

# MARBLES ... ALLYS, MERPS, ETC

These prized little spheroids, (a.k.a. allys, merps, marbses - call 'em what you will) were made of stone, wood, marble (for rich Romans), baked clay, alabaster (hence: "allys"), glass, or steel, and have amused and frustrated billions of kids since since the Garden of Eden where Adam and Eve first flirted with each others nuts and conkers, and, when Adam took a bite out of Eve's dobber, the world's first game ended in a draw - which was precisely what Eve wanted anyway.

These days modern marbles are made of glass, most of them having a little twist of colour inside them which makes them look a bit like a cat's eye (a real cat's eye is more squashy). But you can get them in different sizes and colours which you might call 'besties', and which might be worth two or three of the others (depending on how gullible your pals are). Just have a quick whatsit on the interdoodah.

Nowadays, there are marbles championships held in many parts of the world. And, as with most anoraky types, they take it all very seriously, with strict rules and particular names for all the various little blighters. And they have particular names for all the various little spheroids too. But let us be sensible (no, bugger that, let's not).

As with all street games, no two streets played marbles quite the same way: because every street, especially when they were cobbled, had its own network of holes, nicks, gutters and grids. Therefore, the rules had to be bendy to fit the individual needs of each street and, often, the needs of the individuals. And, more often than not, the kids invented

the rules as they went along. No difference there then.

So, really, anything goes as long we all agree.

You or the kids will probably be inventing and modifying games yourselves after a while. The possibilities are endless.

Meanwhile, here are the basics as handed down through the generations …

---

### Just so you know ...

Standard glass marbles measured about 5/8" (1.5cms) in diameter.

'Dobbers' or 'ponkers' or 'allys' - as we said different names for different places - were about 1" (2.5cms).

Bottle-washers were probably about 1", but you've got a fat chance of finding one of these now, anyway.

Ball-bearings varied but were often outlawed due to their tendency to smash glass ones.

'Besties' were often cloudy or opaque patterned marbles and, like dobbers, worth two or more ordinary ones.

# EQUIPMENT

You don't need much, just marbles - a few or a lot, ordinary and besties. Oh, and perhaps a draw string bag to save wearing holes in your trouser or knicker pockets.

You might also want an ever-useful lolly stick for digging small holes in the ground. I used to wander around after the ice-cream van had gone, picking up discarded lolly sticks to make gliders and to use in lolly stick battles. More about these later in the book.

Get yourself a piece of chalk, slate, or stone with which to draw a circle for some of the marbles games. It will come in handy for hopscotch and a few other games too.  In the terraced streets where I was dragged up there always seemed to be pieces of broken blue roofing slate lying around. Maybe it was seasonal after  winter time, or just the tired old roofs, but it came in handy for all kinds of things. _____

# PLAYING AREA

Dirt, flags, cobbles, concrete, and virtually any flattish surface will do, especially if it has some interesting nicks and holes.

Avoid long grass (for these purposes anyway), and watch out for grids (drains).

Playgrounds aren't recommended because there are possibly dozens of twitchy toe-caps waiting to 'accidentally' boot your marble out of sight.

In dire necessity playing indoors is possible but, unless you have yours on elastic (I've never worked out how to do that), it's a bit of a pain feeling around under settees and sideboards to retrieve them every two minutes. Besides,  wayward marbles have a nasty history of turning up later under your mam's feet whilst she's carrying dad's meat and two veg - painful for everybody!

# PLAYERS & RULES

How many? From one to a mob. All of the sexes can play (boys, girls, and others), and all ages too - although babies tend to prefer to eat them. And do bear in mind that grown-ups can be quite bad losers, so you may have to humour them. Another thing with grown-ups (and reluctantly I have to number myself amongst them) is that we played these games according to our rules as learned aeons ago which, therefore, *must* be better (yawn). But, as I've said, anything goes: old rules, new rules, your rules, someone else's rules, just try to agree at the beginning if you can.

Basically, rules need to be fairly bendy to accomodate who, what, where and why, but a few simple games structures should serve to start you off. Remember, anyone can play, so

let's get going. On second thoughts, let's get **the lingo** sorted before the arguments start ...

**LINGO ~** Names include **Marbses, Aggies, Merps, Allys, Steelies, Dobbers, Bottle-washers**, and more. The marble you flirt or shoot with is called variously **flirter, shooter, taw.** Marbles you shoot *at* are sometimes called **mibs**. Names used for propelling your *flirter-shooter-taw* are: **shooting** (international); **fulking** (provincial schoolboys); **knuckling down** (professionals); and **flirting** (common as muck). The same kind of variety goes for game names  As for me, I'm going to use **marbles, shooters, flirting**, and whatever game names I like. So ner!

# FLIRTING (SHOOTING) YOUR MARBLE

## 1. CHUCKING OR ROLLING

Just take aim and chuck it or roll it. This is ideal for absolute beginners or those who wish to develop their skills towards a career in crown green bowling.

## 2. FINGER FLICKING

Rest your hand on the ground and flick the your flirter with your index finger. Really good for close targets. It's a good idea to practise with peas during school dinner. But not the mushy ones.

## 3. THUMB FLICKING

Balance your marble on the groove between 1st and 2nd fingers. Bring the thumb behind the marble and flick it with your thumb in the direction you want it to go. Watch carefully where it does go and adjust your position accordingly. It's good practice for tossing coins when you're captain of your footie team.

## 4. THUMB FLICKING – POWER VERSION

As with the Thumb Flick but instead of the thumb swinging in space, anchor it to the groove between fingers 2 and 3 just behind the marble. Build up some pressure before springing it to flirt the marble. Stand up for effect, for long shots, or if you get cramp in your legs. Mind the windows.

## 5. FANCY FLIRT (FOR FLASHY PLAYERS)

This is similar to the Power Flirt but the 3rd and 4th fingers stick out. This doesn't improve the flirting of the marble but it looks really cool and does give a significant psychological advantage. Try curling your top lip Elvis-style at the same time. It's quite difficult to do whilst holding a guitar, but it's certainly possible.

*\* It is allowable to simply throw the marbles under or over arm like you might do with a cricket or rounders ball, especially with the bigger ones like dobbers, ponkers and bottle washers. Lads be aware that you may look like a sissy.*

# AND NOW SOME GAMES TO PLAY

### RINGY, RINGO, SHOOT OUT

A circle is drawn on the ground into which each player puts an agreed number of marbles. The players, from behind a line or nick, take turns at flirting their taw at the ones inside the ring. If they knock any out of the ring they keep them and then shoot again from wherever their taw comes to rest. Should any player knock his or her own taw into the ring it remains there as part of the pot and the player begins again with another.

Other 'ring' type games include **RING TAW, KILLER,** or **NEWARK KILLER,** and **FORT** and **BULLSEYE,** which have four circles, one inside the other. Kids have incredibly fertile imaginations, so the list goes on for miles. In **PYRAMIDS** or **CASTLES** the game begins with marbles being stacked up inside the circle, and then continues as before - or differently!

In **SHOOT THE RING** the marbles are placed evenly along the circle circumference and players take it in turns to knock the marbles off it and out of it. If a player misses or or lands their own inside then it goes on the circumference with the others.

All of these can be played indoors using cotton or wool or a shoelace to mark a ring on the carpet or lino.

*Hint:* chalk isn't too popular with parents.

## THREE HOLES

Small holes are scraped in the nicks between cobbles or flags or wherever possible (I got done for practically digging up our backyard once and I can

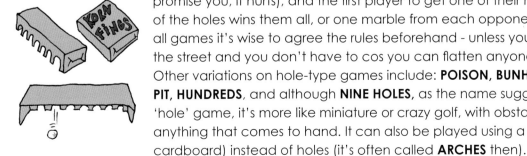

promise you, it hurts), and the first player to get one of their marbles in each of the holes wins them all, or one marble from each opponent ,etc.. As with all games it's wise to agree the rules beforehand - unless you are the cock of the street and you don't have to cos you can flatten anyone who disagrees. Other variations on hole-type games include: **POISON, BUNHOLE, CHERRY PIT, HUNDREDS,** and although **NINE HOLES,** as the name suggests, is another 'hole' game, it's more like miniature or crazy golf, with obstacles made from anything that comes to hand. It can also be played using a arches (cut-out cardboard) instead of holes (it's often called **ARCHES** then).

It's worth getting your cardboard and scissors out because the arches can also be used to play **BRIDGEBOARD** (same idea as **NINE HOLES** but with different rules (surprise surprise!). And instead of a circle, a square is sometimes used, as in **SKELLY** and **DROPSIES.** And a wall is employed in **PUGGY.**

One of the very oldest marbles games (it's those Romans again) is known as **BOSS OUT** by many - also known as **CHASIES** in America, and **SPANNERS** or **NO SPANNERS** In Australia. Being from the north of England, I know it as **HIT AND DOB,** which sounds like a great name for a comedy duo, and can be played just about anywhere ...

## HIT AND DOB

In this really popular game you just flirt your marble at your pal's marble. If you hit it you keep it. Simple, eh? That accounts for the 'hit' bit. But what about the 'dob' job? A 'dob' is the space between one marble and another and can be anything from one to four fingers wide. Therefore 'hit-and-dob' is when one marble hits another and stays close enough to be a 'dob'. In some streets 'hit-and-dob' wins one marble, in other streets it wins two, and so on, but, if a dob occurs without a hit then all things are possible, such as: (i) the dobbed marble is taken, or (ii) the dobbed marble isn't taken, or (iii) the dobbed marble is allowed to escape, or (iv) the dobbed marble is then 'ponked'. Ponked? Yes ponked!

'Ponking' is where, having 'dobbed' your pal's marble, you have another go at it from at least six inches off the ground. If you hit it, you keep it. Ponking requires a steady hand. If you miss it your pals all laugh at you and you go off for a sulk.

Variations on this are even more endless (I know, not very good English - can anything be more endless than endless?). Because to complicate things still further we have 'diders' or 'spans': a 'dider'(pronounced 'die-der') is a space slightly bigger than a dob, and is the gap between the thumb and the little finger of your outstretched hand. A 'stretched dider' is the art of making your dider wider with the use of the other hand.

A 'double dider' is two diders with thumbs touching. Other varieties of diders include a dider-two-fingers, a dider-three-fingers, a dider-four-fingers-and-a-wardrobe (joke), ad confusium. In some streets you may even borrow a mate's fingers to extend a double-dider. When diders occur, one of several hundred things can happen. You can (i) go again or, (ii) have a ponk or, (iii) let your opponent escape or, (iv) go in for your tea, (v) go to Rhyll for your holidays, etc..

NOTE: Diders and obscure rules from other games are often glued together to make life more confusing, but often just to extricate marbles from naiive newcomers.

All of the games can be played 'not-for-keeps', thereby allowing you to play with borrowed marbles. But it's much more fun if you have something to lose!

DAD'S COAT & THE SCRUFFY DOG

# ILLUSTRATED GUIDE TO OUR HERITAGE

# ARCHERY

ARCHERY IS THE ART OF FLIRTING A POINTED PIECE OF WOOD CALLED AN ARROW FROM ANOTHER PIECE OF WOOD WITH A STRING ON CALLED A BOW, AND WAS FIRST INVENTED BY THE CELTS AS A MEANS OF STOPPING SAXON TOURISTS GETTING HOLIDAY HOMES IN THE SNOWDONIAN NATIONAL PARK.

SO POPULAR DID ARCHERY BECOME THAT IT WAS ADOPTED BY OTHER COUNTRIES, THESE FOREIGNERS OFTEN CHANGING THE RULES TO SUIT THEMSELVES.

WILLIAM THE CONQUEROR, FOR EXAMPLE, DECIDED THE HIGHEST POSSIBLE SCORE WAS A "BULL'S EYE" AFTER HITTING THE CAPTAIN OF THE OPPOSING TEAM, HAROLD THE BULL, WITH A STRAY ARROW.

THE MOST FAMOUS ARCHER IN BRITISH HISTORY WAS ROBIN HOOD. IT IS SAID THAT AS HE LAY ON HIS DEATH BED HE CALLED FOR HIS BOW AND SAID "WHEREVER THIS ARROW LANDS, THERE YOU MUST BURY ME". AFTER LOOSING THE ARROW HE DIED.

HE WAS HELD IN SUCH ESTEEM THAT HIS FOLLOWERS CARRIED OUT HIS WISHES AND INTERRED HIM IN THE WASHSTAND.

WILLIAM TELL WAS ANOTHER FAMOUS EXPONENT OF THE GAME, THOUGH HE PREFERRED THE CONTINENTAL CROSSBOW TO THE LONGBOW FAVOURED IN BRITAIN.

HIS PARTY PIECE WAS TO SPLIT AN APPLE BALANCED ON HIS SON'S HEAD. HIS SON'S SUBSEQUENT AVERSION TO PARTIES SAVED HIM A SMALL FORTUNE.

IN THE ELEVENTH AND TWELFTH CENTURIES IT WAS COMPULSORY FOR BOYS ABOVE THE AGE OF EIGHT TO SPEND TIME EACH WEEK PRACTISING ARCHERY IN THE FIELDS AROUND THEIR VILLAGES. THIS CAUSED GREAT DANGER TO COURTING COUPLES, AND MANY SWAINS FELT THE POINT OF AN ARROW IN THE BUTTS.

THE LAST PEOPLE TO TAKE THE SPORT SERIOUSLY WERE THE AMERICAN INDIANS. LIVING ON THE WIDE OPEN PLAINS CAUSED GREAT DIFFICULTIES, AND THEY WERE FORCED TO TRAVEL VAST DISTANCES IN SEARCH OF SUITABLE TARGETS.

TO EASE THE BOREDOM OF THESE JOURNEYS, AND TO KEEP IN PRACTICE, SOME TOOK TO SHOOTING AT THE SETTLERS. UNFORTUNATELY NO-ONE HAD TOLD THEM THAT THE SETTLERS HAD GUNS, WHICH LED TO A RAPID DECLINE IN THE NUMBER OF PEOPLE TAKING PART IN THE SPORT.

WITH THE INVENTION AND DEVELOPMENT OF THE GUN, ARCHERY LOST ITS IMPORTANCE AND HAS SADLY SUNK TO THE STATUS OF A MINORITY SPORT. IT IS PRACTISED NOW BY SO FEW PEOPLE THAT EVEN CHANNEL FOUR DO NOT COVER IT.

# BOWS & ARROWS

Thwap! I can still hear the sound of the arrow sticking to the wall just above my dad's head, early one Christmas morning, as he came to the foot of the stairs to yell "Get back in bed!" at me and our kid. But, by the time I'd seen him, I'd already let the bowstring go and my well-licked rubber-suckered arrow was on its way to parting my dad's hair. Needless to say, we were back in bed in the time it took me to blurt "Sorry dad, my fingers slipped!" And by the time he shouted "And my hand'll slip an' all, in a minute!" me and our kid had burrowed deep under the eiderdown. So, that was the end of that particular bow and arrow. Still, I had a tangerine left.

The next one I had lasted a bit longer. Not a lot longer though: just one day longer. That one was confiscated soon after I shot an arrow through the gap above Freddie Wilcox's outside lav door. Well, I didn't know his mam was in there, did I? So that went on the fire. Nobody argued with Freddie Wilcox's mam: not even Freddie Wilcox's dad.

Me and Freddie had got our bows and arrows from the rag and bone man in return for some old clothes, although Mrs W would have preferred a donkey stone for her step. But, the only rag & bone man you're likely to see now, occasionally drives an old transit van down your street whilst shouting at you through a loudspeaker attached to the van roof. And he's not interested in rags and bones either - scrap metal is what he's after. And what does he give you in return? Nowt. So, there's no point in telling you to nick your dad's old brown mac in order to swap it for a bow and arrow* (or a balloon, or windmill on a stick, or a goldfish). I suppose you can just do the norm, as with everything else, and order one from China via the inter-doodah, but that would cost money.

So why not make one? I've knocked up a really simple and cheap design to get you going and, later on, if you want to get all anoraky you can always wander through the countryside looking for yew, elm, ash, hazel, feathers, flint, beeswax and horsehair. That's what the archers of yesteryear used. And by the time you've made one like that you'll be too tired to play with it. So, let us be realistic.

**YOU'LL NEED** To make a trip to the hardware shop or the garden centre to get...

**For the bow.** A length of cane, about 4ft (1.2m) long - or, if you're lucky enough to find a straight length of springy wood like elm or ash or yew, that would be even better. + Some strong thin string.

**For the arrows.** A few 3ft (0.9m) lengths of thin straight dowel rod, or those little sticks they sell for propping bendy flowers up. + Some twine or strong thread. + A cereal box or thin card from which to cut out the flights.

And you'll need a knife.

**THE BOW** needs to be bendy, so be selective. Cut two notches about two inches (50mm) from each end of the bow. Don't cut them too deep, just enough to stop the bowstring from slipping. Tie your bowstring on using a couple of half hitches, like this:

* To learn more about the rag & bone man listen to The Bradshaws CD1 "In Their Own Words" track 6 "Ragbone & Dad's Brown Mac"

A CHEAP & CHEERFUL BOW & ARROW

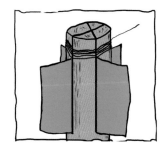

Don't forget to bend the bow as you tie the string on.

**THE ARROWS** should be straight so, as with the bow, be selective. You might perhaps smooth them with sandpaper too, which will help the flight. Usually, arrows have three feathers for the flights but it's much easier to make a cross-cut in the end and insert two pieces of thin card to make four feather-type flights.

First prepare your flights...

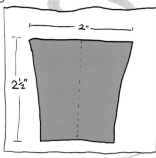

Cut out two of these from your cereal box, or whatever, for each arrow. (It's best to make several arrows in case of breakages). Then crease them lengthways.

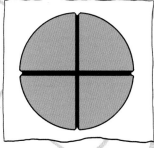

On the flight end of the arrow, carefully make a cross-cut with your knife to about four inches down. I say carefully because, apart from obviously not wanting you to amputate your fingers, you need to avoid splitting the wood.

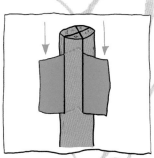

Bend one of your cards so that it will slip down two adjacent slots and so form two of the four flights. Push it down enough to leave a little of the

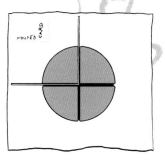

arrow to grip. Repeat that for the other two flights. Then bind the end of the arrow with twine to hold the flights in place. So that they looked authentic, we used to carefully split the tip and put a pointy piece of blue roof slate on to the front end, binding it with twine. Or in the summer, when the pitch was melting on the street, we'd scoop some up with a lolly stick and use that to glue the arrow head on. Anyway, the arrows will fly better if they have a bit of weight added to the tip so, at the very least wrap some insulation tape around the tip end.

**MAKE A TARGET** by stuffing an old jumper with straw or newspaper - but make sure there's nobody wearing the old jumper first!

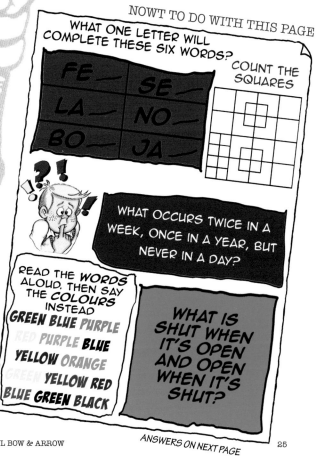

NOWT TO DO WITH THIS PAGE

WHAT ONE LETTER WILL COMPLETE THESE SIX WORDS?

FE—   SE—
LA—   NO—
BO—   JA—

COUNT THE SQUARES

WHAT OCCURS TWICE IN A WEEK, ONCE IN A YEAR, BUT NEVER IN A DAY?

READ THE WORDS ALOUD, THEN SAY THE COLOURS INSTEAD
GREEN BLUE PURPLE
RED PURPLE BLUE
YELLOW ORANGE
GREEN YELLOW RED
BLUE GREEN BLACK

WHAT IS SHUT WHEN IT'S OPEN AND OPEN WHEN IT'S SHUT?

# THE BRADSHAWS in "THE MONKEY WITH THE FUNNY COLOURED BUM"

lf Bradshaw wriggles the big toe that juts out through the hole in his slipper. He stretches and yawns and partially opens the curtain above the sink. He squints as the early morning sunshine barges in and specks of dust glitter and dance about. Far too lively. He closes the curtains again and shouts up the narrow staircase.

"Rise and shine, the morning's fine, the snow'll burn your hair off! Come on dopey, wakey wakey, down the stairs!"

"Erm, hiya dad!"

"Ooh! Don't creep up on me like that," he says to the little face grinning up at him. "Where did you spring from?"

"He-he-hee! Erm, I've been up for hages. I don't know what time I got up, though. It was still dark. I'm hexcited! What time are we goin', dad?"

Billy has obviously dressed himself. His shirt is fastened on the wrong buttons and his pullover is inside out.

"Oh, here we go!" Alf groans. "Mithering Minnie rides again."

"Yeh but, what time *are* we goin', dad?"

"Ask your mother."

Alf turns to shout upstairs again. "Come on, Audrey. The kettle won't boil itself, you know!"

"I'm coming now. Dee-de-dee ..."

A few bars of disembodied and almost tuneless dee-de-dee-ing float around upstairs before a head full of curlers appears round the bedroom door. Audrey's head beams down at him.

"While you're waiting for the waitress, Alf, just give our Billy's shoes a brush, please."

Alf frowns up at Audrey's face. "What did your last slave die of?" he says, a bit weakly.

"Black his best ones and his old ones an' all, will you? And while you're there, Alf, cut some soles out for the old pair 'cause they let water in."

Then, as her curlered head disappears into the bedroom, she shouts "There's an empty Acdo packet under the sink."

The tuneless singing picks up where it left off.

"You're a cheeky sod, Audrey," Alf shouts up at the empty space on the landing. "If you hadn't've spent so long cramming yourself into that frock and complaining about it shrinking, you could've had these shoes done - and mine an' all! I don't know what I pay you for!"

He turns around and almost falls over Billy. Alf growls down at him. "Get out from under my feet, squirt!"

"He-hee! I can see you smiling behind your face! I like it when you're in a good mood, dad."

A few minutes later, still de-de-dee-ing tunelessly, Audrey comes out of the bedroom. Below, Billy lurks just out of sight and counts the twelve creaks as she treads carefully down the stairs. He pounces as she steps off the bottom step and into the kitchen.

"Erm iya mam. Are we goin' to the zoo yet?"

"Oh, good morning, Billy luv," she chimes as she walks past him.

"I'm ready, mam. Look!"

She doesn't, and he emits a disappointed tut.

Alf, from the comfort of his armchair, without a shoe polish tin in sight, and in the absence of any kettle boiling, wastes no time in making a point.

"About time an' all, Audrey! Why does Wittering Willy need his old shoes blacking? We've just bought him new ones."

"Yeh, mam!"

"We?" asks Audrey, as she walks over to the stove. She proceeds to speak to him over her shoulder as she fills the kettle.

"Because Alf, I can't afford to buy him no more this side of Christmas, and if he wears his new ones for going in and his old ones for playing in, his new ones'll still be as good as new when they're old, and his old ones'll last out until the new ones are old, and by then I might be able to afford to buy him new ones. And then I can do the same with the old new ones."

After a slight pause and with a puzzled frown, Alf says, "What?"

Billy stirs it with, "I don't get that. Do you, dad?"

"No, son, I don't."

"He-hee!"

Audrey lights the gas under the kettle.

"So that's why you need to put cardboard in his old ones. It's just common sense."

"If only sense was common!" Alf mutters.

"Does this frock look too tight?" Audrey asks, as she tries to smooth the bumps on her hips.

"I won't be a minute!" Billy shouts as he runs past and up the stairs. "I'm just trying to find my gun in case there's any tigers roamin' round. He-hee!"

"Come on, Alf, you'll have to get a move on. We've got a bus to catch."

"I'm waiting for the men in white coats to appear, my sweet little lunatic."

* *

It's a pleasant enough morning but that doesn't make waiting at a bus stop any more fun, especially when a seven-nearly-eight year old asks, at thirty second intervals, if the bus is coming yet.

After the umpteenth time of asking, Audrey advises him. "A watched bus never boils, luv."

"I know, but ..." grumbles Billy.

Alf is losing the will to live and beginning to get even nowtier.

"Half an hour and not one piggin' bus in sight yet! It's always the ruddy same with the fifty-threes!"

Audrey comes up with another proverb. "Patience is a virgin, Alf."

Then suddenly. "Dad, look, it's comin' now! An' there's two more behind! ... No, three! Quick, let's stick our hands out, and make sure the driver sees us!"

The three of them stick their hands out and the bus trundles to a stop, followed in seconds by the second one and the third - which is completely empty.

"I'm going upstairs. I'm dying for a Woodbine." Alf says as he boards the platform and steps on to the spiral metal steps that wind up to the top deck.

"Can I come, dad?"

"No!" says his disappearing dad.

"Come on, Billy luv, we'll go

downstairs."

"Aw! I want to go hupstairs at the front so I can betend to be the bus driver cos that's what I want to be when I grow hup - as well as a zoo keeper an' all. Aw can I?" Billy pleads.

"Ooh go on then. Be careful!"

"Yeh!" cheers Billy.

"Watch him, Alf!"

Immediately, there's a loud adult male "Oh bloody 'ell!" from somewhere upstairs.

Billy flies up the stairs and Audrey tucks herself into a double seat near the back of the bus. She empties her arms of coats and two shopping bags filled with sandwiches, a flask, plastic cups, and a big bottle of dandelion and burdock flavour fizzy pop, on to the spare seat next to her.

\* \* \*

*A little while later, upstairs at the front ...*

"Are we there yet?" Billy asks yet again. "I fink I can see somefink what might be the zoo!"

With remarkable patience Alf answers. "A couple more stops. See. There's the Scenic Railway," and he points to a giant metal structure on the horizon ahead.

Billy jumaps up and tugs at his dad's arm. "Right, come on, stand hup quick, dad!"

"We've got all day yet. Give over panicking."

"You've got to, dad!"

"What d'you mean, I've *got* to?"

"Erm, cos dad, I want a wee!"

"You should've thought of that before we left the house, shouldn't you? Now you'll have to wait until we get inside."

"I did, dad," Billy whines. "Mi mam made me go an' I shook it an' squeezed it but nuffink come out!"

"You need a washer on it, squirt. *Tut!* Come on then. We'd better go down and stand on the platform in case your valve blows!"

\* \* \*

*A little while and lots of 'Wow, look at that!' later, Alf and Audrey are sitting on a bench while Billy runs about with some other kids nearby.*

"Ooh, it's lovely sitting here in the sunshine, out in the fresh air, int it, Alf?"

"The gasworks'd smell fresh after that elephant house, Audrey,"

"All that walking about has given me an appetite. Are you hungry yet?"

"Hungry?" says Alf, looking sidelong at her. "Well, seeing as all I had for breakfast this morning was an argument, I could eat a bear between two bread vans. You have brought some butties, aven't you?"

"Yes. I've done some of each but they're all mixed up, so it's take your pick 'cause I don't know what'll be in them."

"I do. My teeth. Where are they then?"

"I'll shout our Billy." She stands up and bellows. "*Bil-ly!*"

"Audrey! Warn me before you do that again! How can you afford to put lipstick all the way round that mouth?" To make the point, he wriggles his finger in his ear.

"Billy! Come on! Dinner time!"

"See you in a bit!" Billy shouts to the other kids with whom he's been playing tig, and he runs over to the bench grinning and panting. "He-hee, it's brilliant, int it? Can I 'ave a 'ot dog" *Ple-e-ease?*"

"No luv, I've brought sandwiches, if I can find 'em." Audrey says, as she roots about in a shopping bag.

"Sandwiches? Them in that paper bag? Erm, was they for us?" asks Billy.

Alf scents Billy's sudden nervousness.

THE MONKEY WITH THE FUNNY COLOURED BUM

He nods slowly to himself and mutters "Ey up."

"Yes, but where are they?" says Audrey, as she continues to rummage through the shopping bags.

"Speak, son." Alf says quietly to Billy, who has now begun to crumple before his eyes. Then he moves his face up close to Billy's and adds, intimidatingly, "While you still can."

"Erm, I 'aven't ate 'em. It was that monkey wiv the funny coloured bum!"

"You give my bloody lunch to a baboon?!" Alf snaps.

"Ooh Alf, don't swear. There's people listening!"

"I thought the butties was for the haminals an' I was just givin' the monkey wiv the funny coloured bum a tidgy bit an' it just suddingly snatched the bagful hoff me!"

"Ooh our Billy!"

"How did you get that close to it?"

"Erm, I just climbed hup over the wall."

"It could've pulled your bloody hand off! they're dangerous them things!" Alf says, and he slumps and shakes his head in disbelief.

Audrey looks at it from a slightly different angle - downwards at Billy's feet. "You've been climbing in your best shoes? After all I've said?! *Tut!*"

# YOUR LIFE AND LUCK

## BY GIPSY AGNES WOBBLYBOTTOM *T.L.R., C.P.M.

*Tea Leaf Reader, Clothes Peg Manufacturer (prop.)

## AQUARIUS   PISCES   ARIES

### AQUARIUS (Jan 20 to Feb 18)

*I see a tall dark handsome stranger coming into your life, but any size, shape, or colouring can be arranged (rates negotiable). Meanwhile, you will find yourself in the company of a man who can help you in your career. Go down on bended knee if necessary and then if he refuses you can always nut him in the groin. Generally, the planets are offering you great support right now so enjoy life to the full. Eventually, though, the support will pass and you'll have to rely on your sports bra again. Somebody is not telling you something. Natural psychic awareness should keep you informed. If it doesn't, use the old glass-on-the-wall trick. It never fails.*

### PISCES (Feb 19 to Mar 20)

*You appear to be in control of your career interests at the moment. But the same can't be said of matrimonial or domestic affairs, and you should expect confrontation. Be prepared: wear a gum shield. Financial matters are hilighted now, dear, so take care of business or else the pawnshop might sell the old man's suit. Importantly, a lady who wears a lot of jewellery is the key to your future luck. I have a whole range of lucky charms at very reasonable prices. If you don't hurry up, I may have to see some horrible things in my crystal ball.*

### ARIES (Mar 21 to Apr 20)

*The closeness of Mercury to Venus is causing atmospheric disturbances and making your outlook very unclear. Hang on a minute, my kettle's boiling its head off and my crystal ball is all steamed up! Right, that's better. Romance is in the air and your partner is responding to summer vibrations by showing lots of affection. It's a pity he isn't showing it to you, though. So, hide the dirty old sod's false teeth. On the career front, a job switch is just what you need to make the most of your natural talents. Emptying bins has never been easier. This month could bring you the news you've just been waiting for. If it doesn't, sack the paper boy!*

ANSWERS TO 'NOWT TO DO WITH THIS PAGE' PUZZLES ...

1. W
2. 49 SQUARES
3. THE LETTER 'E'
4. A LEVEL CROSSING

30

FLUFF IN THE LOFT

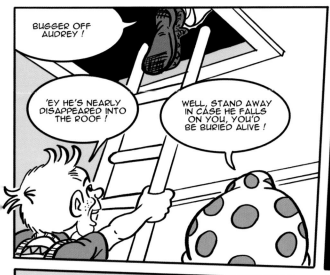

DA-AD !
I DON'T FINK
THEY'RE COMICS

THEY'VE GOT
NAUGHTY LADIES
IN !

AW ! YOU CAN
SEE THEIR
BUSTERS !

'EY
PUT 'EM DOWN !
PUT 'EM DOWN !

THIS ONE'S
IN
COLOUR !

WHAT 'AVE
YOU FOUND,
THEN ?

MAM !

AUDREY !

OOH,
IT'S VERY
MUCKY
UP 'ERE !

IT'S DANGEROUS
AS WELL !
YOU SHOULDN'T BE HERE !
YOU COULD FALL
THROUGH THE CEILING !

'ADN'T YOU BEST GO DOWN, PET ? 'ERE, I'LL 'ELP YOU !

*OOH* HAVEN'T YOU FOUND ANYTHIN' ?

JUST A FEW BOOKS AN' THINGS !

AN' THESE, DAD !

WE'LL GET 'EM DOWNSTAIRS WHERE WE CAN 'AVE A BETTER LOOK, EH ?

THAT'LL BE NICE ALF ! IT'S MORE COMFY DOWN 'ERE !

CAN I 'AVE A PROPER LOOK AS WELL ?

NO, YOU'VE SEEN TOO MUCH AS IT IS !

'COURSE YOU CAN BILLY LOVE !

*HEE! HEE!* FANKS, MAM !

I'LL GO, THEN . . .

RIGHT, BE CAREFUL THEN MY SWEET LITTLE TRIFFID !

FLUFF IN THE LOFT

FLUFF IN THE LOFT

You never know what you might find in the attic - especially other people's attics. Many of the following things may mean nothing at all to you young uns, but ask an older relative or friend and you'll be fascinated by what you find out!

## MEMORY JERKERS

### IF YOU DON'T KNOW JUST ASK AN OLD UN!

HULA HOOPS * SPANGLES * CRAVEN A * OMO FROZEN JUBBLIES * TOBY JUGS * ACDO KALI * DOLLY BLUES * SNAKE BELTS * BREW CANS * WELLY RINGS * GOLLIWOGS * SOCK DARNING * SHERBET LEMONS * LINO * DONKEY STONES * LEAN-TO'S * STICKY-OUT UNDERSKIRTS * PENNY ARROW BARS * LEATHER CASEBALLS * LOTTO * PUSH HALFPENNY * POT DOGS * ZEBO BLACKLEAD * YO-YO'S * TUCKING YOUR FROCK IN YOUR KNICKERS AND DOING HANDSTANDS AGAINST THE WALL * WHITEWASH * THRIPENNY BITS * MANGLES * POSSERS AND DOLLY TUBS * FIVE WOODIES * HIT 'N DOB * DAILY SKETCH * MAVERICK * WAGON TRAIN * BOGEYS * WINKLEPICKERS * SQUARE NECKS * PERRY COMOS * SAMBOS * NUTTY SLACK * TOM MIX * BELLE VUE ZOO * TAPIOCA * POMEGRANETS * THE SPUTNIK * SAT'DAY MATINEES * TURNED-DOWN WELLIES * THE WASH-HOUSE * KNUCKLES * ABC MINORS * THE BELL * AIR-RAID SHELTERS LUDO * RINGLETS * POGO STICKS * TOASTING FORKS * SCHOOL MILK * FREE DINNERS * BREAD AND DRIPPING * TWO PENNETH OF FADES * EGGS WITH A LITTLE LION ON * LUCKY BAGS * MONSTER BAGS * THE POTTY * MUSTARD POULTICE * BILLY BUNTER * UCP TRIPE SHOPS * TRAMSTOPPERS * MAGIC LANTERNS * ACCUMULATORS * BLOW FOOTBALL * CREPE SOLED SHOES * THE TOPPER * THE BEEZER * THE BUNTY * THE RED LETTER * OXYDOL * ALL DAY SUCKERS * TROLLEY BUSES * BLACKJACKS FOUR A PENNY * THE ESSO BLEE DOOLER * VACCINATIONS * FLARED TROUSERS * PENDLETONS TWICERS - ICECREAM WITH A LOLLY EACH END * TOO GOOD TO HURRY MINTS * YOU SHOW ME YOURS AND I'LL SHOW YOU MINE! * TRANSFERS * GUN CAPS * SPUD GUNS * ARROWMINT * PITCH BUBBLES * EATING MUD * BOWS AN' ARROWS OFF THE RAGBONE MAN * A BALLOON OR A WINDMILL ON A STICK IF YOU WERE A SISSY * SUNDAY SCHOOL * THE SCHOLARS * SING SOMETHING SIMPLE * ZEG THE INVINCIBLE * TELLYGOONS * JOHNNY ASTRO * JOHNNY SEVEN * JOHNNY BAGS * JOHNNY MORRIS * GOT GOT NOT GOT * U.N.C.L.E. BADGES * THE MUSICAL MUSCLEMAN * WARMING MILK ON SCHOOL RADIATORS * ICICLES ON THE WINDOWS * TANGERINES AND NUTS IN YOUR CHRISTMAS STOCKING * HUNGRY HORACE * FREE PACKET OF BEECH NUT WHEN THE ARROW POINTED FORWARD (AND WAITING ROUND THE CORNER IN CASE SOMEBODY FORGOT) * MILKY BAR KID * FREE MILK * FREE DINNERS * NATIONAL HEALTH GLASSES * STICKY BUDS * LAMPLIGHTERS * FRUITS SALADS * HALF A CROWN

# LOLLY STICKS ... FINGS TO DO WIV 'EM

Heven if you ant got no lolly sticks, not even one, well thats alrite, cos you can just tek some bockles back to the shop an get some money, and then you can by a lolly from granellis hicecreem van or from the corner shop.  But, if you ant got no bockles, well, you can just run a herrand for missis nutall, but tell her you dont wont a happle and then she mite give you sum money for a hicecreem, so you can ave the stick... Right?

Hokay, here is sum fings to do wiv lolly sticks wot Ive made up miself wivout no help from nobody epseptin mi dad a bit.

One good fing is to ave a lolly stick fite wiv yur frend hoos got a lolly stick, but dont play it wiv yur frend hoo ant got no lolly stick cos he mite want one of yurs to ave a fite wiv, and thats no good is it?  You just see hoo goes ferst by avin a hargument or sumfink, and then one of you olds his lolly stick at bofe ends in front of em and the huvver hits it wiv his lolly stick.  If it dunt brayk, the huvver one has a tern and you just keep goin til one brayks, thats all, but... mind you dont bash yur fingers up like I dun wen mi frend hit me, but he dint do it on perpus he sed.

If youv honly got one lolly stick, well you can make yur toy soljers or toy cowboys and hinjuns walk the plank, or... you can sit on the flags houtside yur ouse and scrape the dirt from between em, just in case you feel like it, or... you can balans yur stick on a bobbin of coton and hav it as a seesaw for yur toy soljers, or... you can flote yur stick in a puggle houtside and try and bom it wiv stones, but it wont never sink, or...

GOODY

BOOK
TO HOLD
IT DOWN

BADDY

I fink it shud be called **"HOW TO MAKE YOUR MEASLY SPENDS STRETCH EVEN MORE FURVERER"** by Billy Bradshaw (an' mi dad a bit)"

You can just flirt it easy peasy wivout even a lastic band by mi own hinvenshen, like this - you put yur hand flat on the table and put the stick standin up between yur fingers and pull it back and just let it go, thats all. (I can hit mi mam wen shes at the sink from the huvver side of our table, so ner!), or...

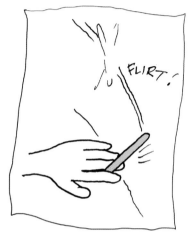

You can make a choon on the table by pressin yur lolly stick down wiv a bit stickin out and boyngin it, or...

If youv got five lolly sticks, you can make a lolly stick glider. Its hard to tell you how, so mi dads drawd a picher for you, or...

You can make a raft for yer toy soljers to cross over the river wiv, but not a reel river, cos mi mam sed you mite fall in.

Mi dad tole me that sum one even bilt a blackpool tower model wiv lolly sticks. That'd be hard tho.

See, so you can hav lods of fun wiv just lolly sticks, carnt you? That's all, so ner!

Dear Audrey,
I'm a poor student living off a grant, and, knowing what a wonderful, nay, miraculous job you do coping off the measly amounts Alf gives you, I am hoping you can give me some advice on how to manage and what are the best bargains from the corner shop.
Yours hungrily, Andrew Brookes, Maltby, S. Yorks

Dear Andrew,
you poor thing! The first thing to do is try to keep warm now that the bad weather's coming. Patch the holes in your trousers and tuck your vest in your underpants to keep your workings warm, and seeing as you do a lot of brainwork try to keep your head warm. That's why you should always eat your crusts cos they make your hair curly and that keeps your brains warm, doesn't it? I always have a perm for winter cos I can't eat crusts cos of my teeth moving about making my gums sore. You can do a lot with a little, so make stew and dumplings, and neck end and pea soup. That keeps Alf going. And remember to fill up with bread. Oh yis, look for the stall on the market what sells broken biscuits and have them with warm milk for pudding.

# TELL AUDREY ALL ABOUT IT
**Audrey Bradshaw's Problem Page**
(after living with Alf all these years I'm qualified to protrude into people's affairs)

Dear Audrey,
when I first got married my husband was happy to stop in and spend the evenings alone with me. We would entertain ourselves playing card games and such like. Now I hardly see him at all except when he rolls in from the pub and falls up the stairs to bed. I miss our time together and so do the triplets, John, Jamie, and Joey, and our twin girls, Jenny and Janine. Even the cats, Mickey, Mary, and Montmerency, fail to recognise him sometimes, and only last Thursday night one of the dogs bit him, thinking him to be a burglar. What can I do?
Mrs Jean Innershoe, Bootle, Lancs.

Dear Jean,
I can't hardly understand any man wanting to be out all the time, specially when they've such a lovely family like what you have at your house. Mind you, most men are funnyosities anyway, so it's hard to understand anything they do. You could try what a friend of mine did the other week. She got fed up of waiting for hers to come home for his Sunday dinner so she took it to him at the pub. It worked cos he got barred by the landlady for getting food all over the seats. But if you try that, make sure you wear a rainhat cos the gravy ruined her perm.

Dear Audrey,
I know you're not a doctor but you seem to have an understanding of general homey-type problems like house-maid's knee, mumps, tonsilitus, and that sort of thing. Well, I'll come to the point: I have this embarassing itching, you see. It's bad enough when I'm stood up but It's practically impossible to get at when I'm sat down, without contorting myself like a contortionist. I'd appreciate your advice on the matter. Thanks in anticipation,
Yours, Dawn B.Lowe, Happy Valley, Hants.

Dear Dawn,
I think I know what might just be causing your itchyness. I bet you've got some of them bri-nylon knickers, haven't you? Well, they're alright until you go to bed in 'em... that's when they end up full of little hard balls of bed fluff and they do tend to itch - they did me! Chuck 'em out right away, even if you've nowt else to put on yet! My best friend Betty Morris often goes without, but she never goes upstairs on the bus. I couldn't do it myself though! Alf (I didn't tell him your name) suggested you made a scratcher out of one of them new-fangled wire coat hangers and bent it straight with a little bit turned up at the end, but you'd have to be careful!

Dear Audrey,
being a mother yourself you might understand my predicament. My six month old baby son Robert seems to be able to output twice as much as he inputs and as changing his nappy makes me billious I'd do any-thing to avoid it. I sealed him up once with elastoplast but he blew it right off. I love my son but I'm at the end of my tether. Please help.
Frank Leesik, Barcup, Lancs.

Dear Frank,
I realise it isn't easy being a mother when you're a man, so I'll write slowly. Babies can't eat the same food as grown-ups and I noticed your letter smelled of curry. Being a working mother is hard and it might seem easier to give your Robert a bit of what you have, but it isn't a good idea. Curry and chips and a bottle of brown ale is fine for you but Robert needs a rusk now and then. I think you should find yourself a nice widow. Alf thinks you should change Robert under water cos it works with onions, but take no notice!

TELL AUDREY ALL ABOUT IT...
IF YOU DON'T WANT TO GIVE YOUR NAME
YOU CAN JUST BE UNANIMOUS

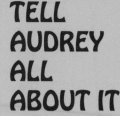

Dear Audrey,

last summer I went on a Young At Heart Club holiday to Benidorm and had a wonderful time reminiscing with other members about the old days. I danced that much that I sprained my zimmer frame, but it was worth it. There was a handsome waiter called Pedro with a twinke in his eye. I knew he fancied me because of the great big portions of chips and extra sausages he slipped me at dinnertimes. Sadly, we didn't get close enough because of his garlicky breath making me billious. I'm determined to go back so we can fulfil our hearts' desires, but how can I overcome the barrier that came between us last time?

Dolly Blue, (93 years young), Longsight, Manchester.

Dear Dolly,

when I first met my Alf he was always eating pickled onions and it took years to get used to the pong. My friend Ada had the same problem with her Joe but it wasn't too bad because he made her wear a paper bag over her head, which shows men can be thoughtful sometimes. If you wear one, be careful when you're dancng then you won't fall over your handbag and hurt yourself like Ada did. By the way, Sloan's Linament is very good for sprains.

**AUDREY BRADSHAW**

S.W.A.L.K.

Dear Senora Audrey,

I havva the bigga problemo. Last year una olda biddy have com to mio hotel for holiday. She chasa me eferywar tryin for to sticka da lips ona me. Alla de time olda biddy want for dansa and I am, how your Alfredo say, knackered. Still my foots are hurt me with bigga walka frame jumpa ona mio bigga toe. I giva olda biddy mucho chip and chipolato for try slow lady down, but no. In finale I am eata mucho garlico and it make me sick cosa I am hate garlico, but it not stoppa olda biddy. I frite she com agen mio hotel. Plees assista.

Pedro Lopeza, Hotel Bonco, Benidorm, Espana.

Dear Pedro,

you're not a good speller, are you? I couldn't hardly understand a word of your letter. I'm sending you our Billy's Janet and John Book One, cos he's finished with it now, so you'll be able to write proper English. I hope this helps you.

LOVED THROUGHOUT THE WORLD BY KNITTED SCARF MANUFACTURERS AND THROAT LOZENGE SALESMEN, FOOTBALL HAS, AMONGST OTHER THINGS, LENGTHENED WEDDINGS, SHORTENED MARRIAGES, AND INSPIRED THE INVENTION OF THE PLASTIC BEER GLASS – AND IT ALL BEGAN HERE!

LET'S LOOK AT ...

# FOOTBALL

THROUGHOUT HISTORY NO OTHER SPORT HAS INFLAMED THE PASSIONS MORE THAN FOOTBALL! MATCHES WERE OFTEN PLAYED BETWEEN RIVAL VILLAGES WITH EVERYONE IN THE VILLAGE TAKING PART

FOLLOWING THE SHEEP AND COW BLADDER ACT OF 1652, UNDER WHICH IT BECAME AN OFFENCE TO KICK A DEAD ANIMAL'S BLADDER, THE BLADDER WAS HIDDEN INSIDE A LEATHER CASE, BUT THE CORNERS MADE IT AWKWARD TO CONTROL.

THESE GAMES OFTEN DEGENERATED INTO VIOLENCE AND THUS THE GAME WE KNOW AND LOVE TODAY WAS BORN.

EARLY RECORDS SHOW THAT THE GAME WAS ORIGINALLY PLAYED WITH A SHEEP OR COW'S BLADDER. THE WEAKEST MEMBER OF THE TEAM WAS TRADITIONALLY ELECTED TO BLOW THIS UP USUALLY BY THE STRONGER MEMBERS.

THE PROBLEM WAS SOLVED BY SAM SHUTTLEWORTH WHO FOUND THAT HIS WIFE'S CHRISTMAS PUDDINGS ROLLED BETTER AND WERE TEN TIMES STRONGER.

HIS WIFE ONLY FOUND OUT ABOUT HIS SECRET INCOME AFTER HIS DEATH. WHEN GOING THROUGH HIS PERSONAL BELONGINGS SHE DISCOVERED FORTY EMPTY PUDDING BAGS AND SEVENTY FIVE CLAIMS FOR HEAD INJURIES.

SOME TEAMS STILL USE PUDDINGS TODAY. ONE WAS RECENTLY TRANSFERRED TO EUROPE FOR A LARGE SUM OF MONEY.

# REMEMBER ... REMEMBER

(Not just for old farts. You can always memorize these for the pub quiz!)

50 -ISH YEARS AGO ... BRITAIN INTRODUCED A 70MPH SPEED LIMIT AND BANNED CIGGIE ADVERTS ON TELLY WHILST RHODESIA DECLARED INDEPENDENCE, THE 250 MILE PENNINE WAY WAS OPENED, AND THE BEATLES WENT TO NUMBER ONE WITH "TICKET TO RIDE", "HELP", "DAYTRIPPER" AND "WE CAN WORK IT OUT".

55 YEARS AGO ... ROUGHLY "APACHE", "POOR ME", "RUNNING BEAR", AND "MY OLD MAN'S A DUSTMAN" MADE THE TOP SPOT IN THE POP CHARTS AS BRITAIN LOST THE FARTHING AND GAINED "CORONATION STREET", THE NUCLEAR-POWERED SUB "DREADNOUGHT" AND THE DREADED TRAFFIC WARDENS.

60+ YEARS AGO ... BRIT CHRISTOPHER COCKRELL PATENTED THE HOVERCRAFT, JAMES DEAN DIED AGED 24, STEVE OVETT WAS BORN AGE 0, CHURCHILL RESIGNED AS PRIME MINISTER PERHAPS IN PROTEST AT JIMMY YOUNG TOPPING THE CHARTS WITH "THE MAN FROM LARAMIE"!

65 YEARS AGO ... GIVE OR TAKE IN THE YEAR WHEN SOAP AND PETROL RATIONING DIED AND LEGAL AID, PRINCESS ANN, BARRY SHEENE, ANDY PANDY AND THE ARCHERS WERE BORN, 199,850 WATCHED THE BRAZIL V URUGUAY WORLD CUP FINAL IN RIO AND THE KOREAN WAR BEGAN.

# I NAME THIS CHILD HERBERT

How many parents have gazed with damp eyes over the side of the cot at their beautiful, tiny-toed, gurgling, newly born who had never harmed a soul, and decided to call him Herbert or Humphrey or Horace. it's hard to believe but they did! The girls were no better off either, being landed with monikers like Deidre, Doris, and Ermintrude. The funny thing is though, generally, older people tend to suit their names, whatever they are. Perhaps they grow into them?
Take mine for instance...

## AND THEN THERE'S THE MEANING OF NAMES

TITUS
A DUCK'S SPHINCTER
IGNATIUS
LAMPLIGHTER
JACOB
CRACKERS
SOPHIE
LIKES IT ON THE SETTEE
ALISTAIR
LIKES IT ON THE LANDING
LETITIA
'D' CUP

CHARMAINE
FRIED NOODLES
AMANDA
BLOKE IN A FROCK
HENRY
CHICKEN COOP
BERTHA
MOORS SHIPS FOR A LIVING
CORA
LIKES APPLES
CHARLOTTE
DRINKS GALLONS OF TEA

LUKE
OBSERVER, VOYEUR
WALLY
DERIVATIVE OF 'WALL'. THICK AS A BRICK
AND FINALLY...
AUDREY
(ACCORDING TO BILLY)
SHORT FOR 'AUDREYNARY')
(AS DEFINED BY ALF) FROM THE FRENCH 'AU' MEANING 'TO THE', AND 'DREY' OR 'DRAY' MEANING 'CART'.
THEREFORE AU-DREY 'TO THE CART' OR 'HORSEY'.

# FRED THE TED

## MEMORY JERKERS
### IF YOU DON'T KNOW JUST ASK AN OLD UN!

COLTSFOOT ROCK * CHAPPED LEGS * RIN TIN TIN * LASSIE * TOE RAGS * THE JACKIE * MUFFIN THE MULE * MILLICAN AND NESBITT * THE PARTRIDGE FAMILY * INKWELL MONITOR * BEATLE JACKETS * MEET THE HUGGETS * RAY GUNS * RICKETS * YURI GAGARIN * LANRY * ADAM ANT * JUNGLE JIM * DERBAC NIT COMBS * OVALTEENIS * GOLOSHES * SPIN THE BOTTLE * ONE POTATO TWO POTATO THREE POTATO FOUR * WINTER WARMERS * DOING THE BEND CRAB * CRIMPLENE * THE NIT NURSE * CROTCHETED DRESSES * PONCHOS * ZORRO * THE DODGEMS * THE SLOSH * BIFF BATS * KALEIDOSCOPES * IRMA OGDEN * CLACKERS * AUSTIN A40'S * COAL EGGS * TINY TIM * THE WOODENTOPS * TROLLEY BUSES * DRIPPING BUTTIES * LICORISH STICKS * SLOAN'S LINAMENT * DISTEMPER * APACHE * COWHEEL * JELLY BABIES * GONKS * CRAZY FOAM * THE ARMY GAME * BOOTSIE AND SNUDGE * MONICA ROSE * FOUR FEATHER FALLS * SUPERCAR * OIL CLOTH * BRAINS TRUST * BUFFALO BILL * THE TROGGS * POWER CUTS * TUPPERWARE PARTIES * PEDAL CARS * FREDDIE FRINTON * BUBBLE CARS * PREFABS * STREET PARTIES * MARY HOPKINS * SUGAR BUTTIES * HUSH PUPPIES * CARBOLIC * STEAM TRAINS * CLINIC GLASSES * THE BOARD DUSTER * SPUD GUNS * CABBAGE AND RIBS * PLASTIC TABLE CLOTHS * HIPSTERS * A RIDE ON THE CROSSBAR OF A BIKE * TUCKING YOUR FROCK IN YOUR KNICKERS * SADDLE SORE * GAS LAMPS * WHIP-AND-TOPS * WOODWORK LESSONS * THE STRAP * SCHOOL MILK * SEMOLINA * POUNDS, SHILLINGS & PENCE * CAMOMILE LOTION * BREAD POULTICES * TIMES TABLES * DOCTORS AND NURSES * PIMPLES * PADDED BRAS * RUBBER SHEETS * PLAYING WAG * FORGING A NOTE FROM YOUR MAM * PLAYING CHICKEN * SLACK UNDERPANTS * WENDY HOUSES * SYRUP OF FIGS * PITCH BUBBLES * VACCINATIONS * LEAD SOLDIERS * BUBBLY GUM IN YOUR HAIR * ASKING FOR YOUR BALL BACK * LEARNING TO SMOKE * TRYING TO GET IN FOR AN 'X' * DINNER LADIES * FLITTING * CLUEDO * PAKAMACS * PONTEFRACT CAKES * TIT-BITS * DRAPE JACKETS * BAY CITY ROLLERS * KIT CARSON * BARBIE DOLL

# PAPER CHASE ... OUTDOOR FUN!

As with lots of street games, this one often starts with, "You're under my feet! Go and play out while it's still light. You'll be complaining you want to stay out when it's time to come in, if you ever go out!" Or words to that effect. But before you do go out, have one last mither for some paper and a pencil because you'll need it for this.

You can make this as complicated as you like but basically, these are the rules:
Team One hides the clues.
Team Two finds them.

It might go like this…

THE TEAMS HAVE A SHORT ARGUMENT, OR A GAME OF SCISSORS-WRAP-STONE, OR WHICH-HAND-HAVE-I-GOT-THE-STONE-IN, TO DECIDE WHO GOES FIRST.

AFTER SOME WHISPERING AND SCRIBBLING AND SNIGGERING, TEAM ONE RUN OFF TO HIDE SEVERAL PIECES OF PAPER. ON EACH PIECE OF PAPER THEY HAVE WRITTEN DIRECTIONS OR A CLUE TO WHERE THE NEXT PIECE OF PAPER IS HIDDEN.

TEAM ONE HAND A PIECE OF PAPER CONTAINING THE FIRST CLUE TO TEAM TWO, THUS…

*MISTER BONSALL'S CORNER SHOP*

TEAM TWO RUN OFF SCREAMING LIKE MANIACS TO SEARCH IN THE VICINITY OF MISTER BONSALL'S CORNER SHOP. THEY EVENTUALLY FIND THE PIECE OF PAPER FOLDED UP IRRITATINGLY SMALL AND SHOVED INTO THE LITTLE GAP UNDER MR BONSALL'S WINDOW SILL. THEY RETRIEVE IT AFTER SOME SERIOUS POKING ABOUT WITH A LOLLY STICK AND READ IT…

ONCE AGAIN THEY ALL RUN OFF LIKE LUNATICS UP THE ENTRY TO THE BACK OF NUMBER 17 WHERE SOMEBODY HAS TO CLIMB OVER THE BACK

*NUMBER 17 BACKYARD. ASK BONZO*

DOOR TO LET THE OTHERS IN. FORTUNATELY, BONZO IS A FRIENDLY DOG WITH NO TEETH, SO, AT WORSE, HE MIGHT JUST GIVE SOMEONE A BIT OF A NASTY SUCK. UNFORTUNATELY, BONZO HAS MORE SPIT THAN HIS MOUTH WILL HOLD AND PROCEEDS TO SLAVER ALL OVER SOMEBODY'S HAND AS THEY RETRIEVE THE NOTE FROM UNDER THE DOG'S BOWL. IT TAKES A WHILE TO DECIPHER THE WRITING ON THE NOTE WHICH IS NOW BLURRED DUE TO THE COATING OF DOG SPIT. FINALLY, THEY READ…

A TEAM WHINGE GOES UP, "AW NO! IT'S NOT FAIR! WE'LL GET DONE NOW OFF NAGGY OLD JACKSON FOR CLIMBING UP THE LAMP

*UP THE LAMP POST OUTSIDE Mrs JACKSON'S*

POST. SHE THINKS SHE OWNS THE STREET! LET'S CHUCK A WATER BOMB OVER HER BACKYARD!" ETC..

A PROPER PAPER CHASE

# YOUR LIFE AND LUCK

## BY GIPSY AGNES WOBBLYBOTTOM *T.L.R., C.P.M.
*Tea Leaf Reader, Clothes Peg Manufacturer (prop.)

## TAURUS   GEMINI   CANCER

### TAURUS (Apr 21 to May 20)

I see a tall dark stranger in my crystal ball, and if you so much as look at him I'll punch your lights out. But romance is in the stars for you and you could be asked to go on a blind date. It's probably the best kind too, with your looks, dear. You'll be amazed at how well you can cope with a problem at work, but an official letter must be written now. And if you still don't get a raise, show him the photos but hang on to the negatives. Beware though, you're just a little gullible at the moment so just be careful that nobody takes you for a ride. Mind you, you'd probably enjoy it anyway. You always were the town bike.

### GEMINI (May 21 to Jun 20)

The proximity of Pluto to one of the other planets (I can't think which one it is just now) will cause some distress to your financial affairs for quite some time to come. Take action. Buy plenty of candles and get a wind-up gramophone, or maybe even flit before the bailiffs come around. But cosmic forces will give you the courage to push one of your long-cherished ambitions. Get the swine to walk nearest the canal next time. Romance is here, though, you lucky old tart, and Venus will soon be popping into your sign with a bit of passion. So dig out your lacey ones and pucker up. And as for you girls …

### CANCER (Jun 21 to Jul 20)

You'll be feeling the effects of the moon's pull over the next few days, so put a thick woolley cardigan on if you must go outside to howl at it. Your paitience will be tested towards the end of the month, so try to make allowances. P.M.T. is a two-way problem. Cancerian girls, you seem to be in a bit of a mess lately and you could do with ironing a few things out. Get him to fix the rope on your clothes rack and then the washing won't keep sliding down to one end and getting all creased up. Cancerian boys, the tablets seem to be working and you feel you can do anything. This might be the time to make changes around the house. Empty the drawers before you try to shift the sideboard, or tighten your truss - you don't want to be off work again.

## "CRASH DIET"

KING KONG, THE AMAZING APE OF ANGER IS ON THE LOOSE! THE SAVAGE JUNGLE BEAST WANTS REVENGE AGAINST MICHAEL MORRIS THE WHITE HUNTER WHO KILLED MRS KONG AND HER TWO BABIES . . .

CRASH DIET

CRASH DIET

CRASH DIET

CRASH DIET

OH-OH! PEOPLE SIT DOWN TO EAT CAKE... EVEN WEDDIN' CAKE!

ARE WE GONNA EAT IT NOW BEFORE WE SIT DOWN? IT'LL BE DEAD GOOD, JUST LIKE *STANDIN' UP* AT A PARTY!

WHAT ARE YOU YABBERING ON ABOUT NOW? I SWEAR HE'S PUDDLED!

OH, WHAT A CRUEL THING TO SAY! YER SHOULDN'T SPEAK LIKE THAT ABOUT YER OWN!

WELL, WHY INT *SHE* EATIN' IT? DOES SHE KNOW SUMMAT WE DON'T? I'VE NEVER SEEN 'ER PASS UP FOOD BEFORE, MUCH LESS GIVE IT AWAY!

WE OUGHT TO 'AVE IT TESTED FOR RAT POISON! SHE'S PROBLY TRYIN' TO DO AWAY WITH US 'COS OF THE NOISE YIPPERIN' JONNY MAKES WHEN HE CALLS ROUND!

MY NAME'S BILLY BUT I WOULDN'T MIND BEIN' CALLED *JOHNNY SEVEN*! HE! HE!

ADA'S NOT LIKE THAT ANYMORE. SHE'S ON A DIET FROM THE DOCTOR AN' 'ER JOE WON'T LET 'ER 'AVE NONE!

I DON'T BLAME 'IM, EITHER! THE FAT SOD!

WON'T GIVE 'ER WHAT? FOOD?

NEVER YOU MIND WHAT SHE'S NOT GETTIN'! YOU SHOULDN'T BE LISTENIN' TO GROWN UPS!

I WAS ONLY ASKIN'!

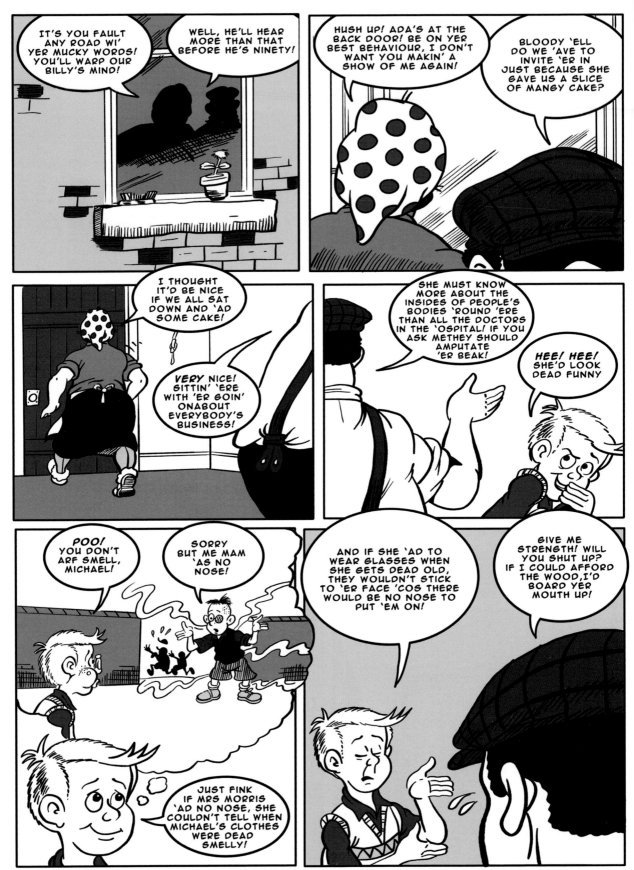

CRASH DIET

CRASH DIET

# ILLUSTRATED GUIDE TO OUR HERITAGE

*LOOKING BACK FONDLY AT THE DEVELOPMENT OF THE OUTSIDE LAV (BOG, KARZI, LOO, PRIVVY, JAKES, COMFORT STATION, THRONE ROOM, CLOSET, OR - FOR OUR OVERSEAS READERS - DUNNY OR JOHN)*

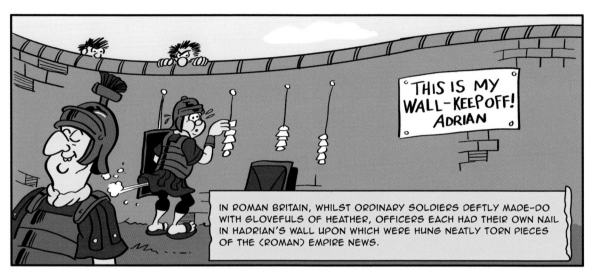

'THIS IS MY WALL-KEEP OFF!' ADRIAN

IN ROMAN BRITAIN, WHILST ORDINARY SOLDIERS DEFTLY MADE-DO WITH GLOVEFULS OF HEATHER, OFFICERS EACH HAD THEIR OWN NAIL IN HADRIAN'S WALL UPON WHICH WERE HUNG NEATLY TORN PIECES OF THE (ROMAN) EMPIRE NEWS.

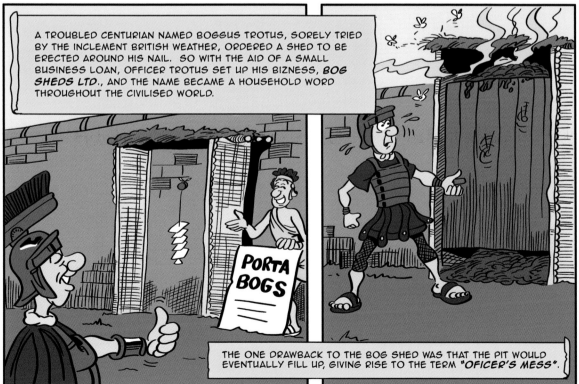

A TROUBLED CENTURIAN NAMED BOGGUS TROTUS, SORELY TRIED BY THE INCLEMENT BRITISH WEATHER, ORDERED A SHED TO BE ERECTED AROUND HIS NAIL. SO WITH THE AID OF A SMALL BUSINESS LOAN, OFFICER TROTUS SET UP HIS BIZNESS, *BOG SHEDS LTD.*, AND THE NAME BECAME A HOUSEHOLD WORD THROUGHOUT THE CIVILISED WORLD.

PORTA BOGS

THE ONE DRAWBACK TO THE BOG SHED WAS THAT THE PIT WOULD EVENTUALLY FILL UP, GIVING RISE TO THE TERM *"OFICER'S MESS"*.

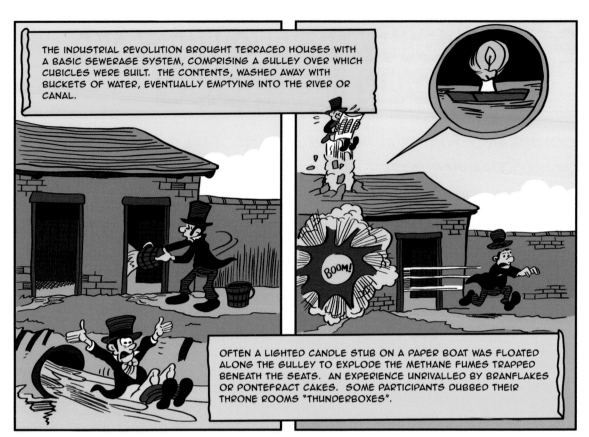

THE INDUSTRIAL REVOLUTION BROUGHT TERRACED HOUSES WITH A BASIC SEWERAGE SYSTEM, COMPRISING A GULLEY OVER WHICH CUBICLES WERE BUILT. THE CONTENTS, WASHED AWAY WITH BUCKETS OF WATER, EVENTUALLY EMPTYING INTO THE RIVER OR CANAL.

OFTEN A LIGHTED CANDLE STUB ON A PAPER BOAT WAS FLOATED ALONG THE GULLEY TO EXPLODE THE METHANE FUMES TRAPPED BENEATH THE SEATS. AN EXPERIENCE UNRIVALLED BY BRANFLAKES OR PONTEFRACT CAKES. SOME PARTICIPANTS DUBBED THEIR THRONE ROOMS "THUNDERBOXES".

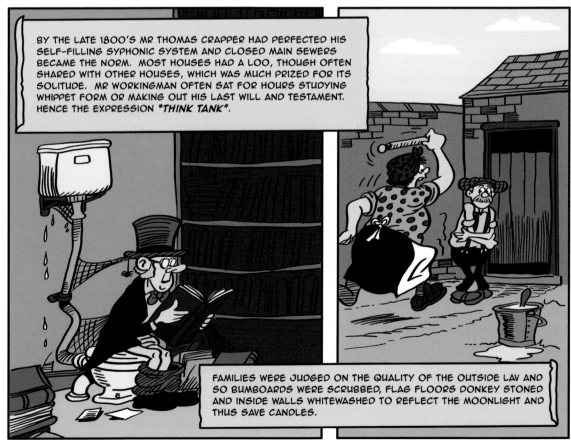

BY THE LATE 1800'S MR THOMAS CRAPPER HAD PERFECTED HIS SELF-FILLING SYPHONIC SYSTEM AND CLOSED MAIN SEWERS BECAME THE NORM. MOST HOUSES HAD A LOO, THOUGH OFTEN SHARED WITH OTHER HOUSES, WHICH WAS MUCH PRIZED FOR ITS SOLITUDE. MR WORKINGMAN OFTEN SAT FOR HOURS STUDYING WHIPPET FORM OR MAKING OUT HIS LAST WILL AND TESTAMENT. HENCE THE EXPRESSION *"THINK TANK"*.

FAMILIES WERE JUDGED ON THE QUALITY OF THE OUTSIDE LAV AND SO BUMBOARDS WERE SCRUBBED, FLAG FLOORS DONKEY STONED AND INSIDE WALLS WHITEWASHED TO REFLECT THE MOONLIGHT AND THUS SAVE CANDLES.

# BAZZIN' PAPER PLANES

## INDOORS OR OUTDOORS YOU CAN HAVE SOME GREAT FUN WITH PAPER PLANES HERE ARE SOME ACE DESIGNS FOR YOU TO MAKE EASY PEASY!

I FINK YOU'RE GOIN' TO LIKE THESE BAZZIN' PAPER HAROPLANES!

COS I DO! HE-HEE!

If you've ever been to one of my Bradshaws live theatre shows (and if you haven't, why not?) you will have had a bit of practice at making paper aeroplanes.

All you need are some sheets of paper, so that's cheap enough, isn't it? A4 is about the right size and they can be lined or plain, white or coloured (coloured is cool.) I've designed these planes with A4 sheets in mind but as long as they are rectangular and big enough (the size of the pages in this book, perhaps?) they will still fly. And if you haven't got any A4 paper and you're really skint (aw!) and can't afford to buy any cos your spends are too measly (like Billy's), you can make your planes from some sheets of newspaper, and they look good too! Just have a root under the armchair cushion and you might find some. Magazine pages tend to be of heavier paper and, unless you make a huge one, they won't fly as well. **HINT:** Make sure your old fella has finished the crossword and your mam doesn't want it for tearing into squares and hanging in the lav!

There are four designs on the next few pages for you to try: 'The Nipper', 'The Superdart', 'The Martian Spacecraft', and 'The Hawk'. Then there's a page of dead good tips and tricks for how to get the best out of your bazzin' paper planes. All of them are easy to make and, with a bit of tweaking, they are all good flyers. And I've had a bazzin' time experimenting and testing them. Have fun!

# HOW TO MAKE BAZZIN' PAPER AEROPLANES
# THE 'NIPPER'

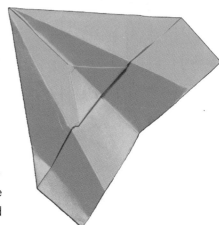

The Nipper is easy to make and is one of the best long-distance gliders around. If you chuck it out of your bedroom window, it's likely to be still in the air when you run out of your door on to the street - providing your bedroom isn't in the cellar.

I find that this plane flies best using a slower launch speed. Instead of bringing your arm back over your shoulder and chucking it like a javeline, throw it from just in front of your face with a smooth action. And try slightly turning up the flaps at the back. With the right velocity throw you can make it swoop and come right back to you.

I often go out hill-walking in the High Peak, Derbyshire, and one of my favourite walks involves a struggle up a steep track on to the ridge above Shining Clough. I always make sure to prepare a few paper planes to take out with me - or at least, put an A4 pad in my rucksack. And it's fantastic to sit chucking paper planes from a few hundred feet up and to watch Ihem glide for ages down to the ground below (Yes, before you start, I do my best to pick my litter up later).

The Nipper is ideal for long glides.

## HOW TO MAKE 'THE NIPPER'

1. FOLD IN HALF LENGTHWAYS TO FIND THE CENTRE LINE. SOFTLY CREASE IT, THEN OPEN IT FLAT AGAIN

2. FOLD ONE CORNER INTO THE CENTRE LINE

3. FOLD THE SECOND CORNER INTO THE CENTRE LINE

4. FOLD THE POINT DOWN TO APPROX 1" (2.5 CM) FROM THE BOTTOM. IT SHOULD LOOK LIKE AN ENVELOPE AS IN THE DRAWING BELOW

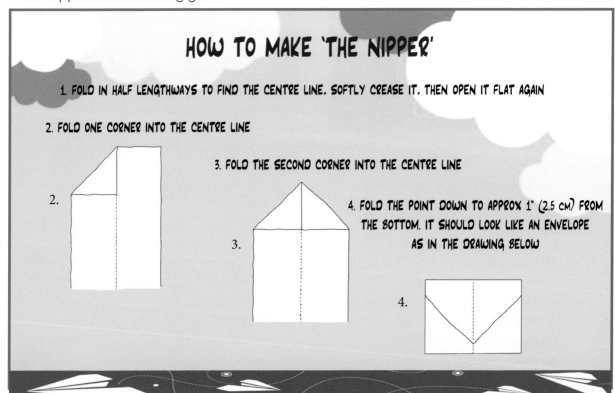

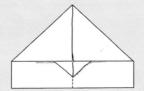

## TO MAKE 'THE NIPPER' CONT'D

**5. FOLD THE SECOND SET OF CORNERS INTO CENTRE. MAKE SURE THERE IS A TRIANGULAR POINT STICKING OUT BELOW**

5.

**6. FOLD THE TRAINGULAR POINT UP TO HOLD THE CORNERS DOWN**

6.

**7. FOLD BACKWARDS IN HALF ALONG THE SPINE, LEAVING THE TRIANGULAR STICKY-OUT BIT ON THE OUTSIDE**

7.

**8. FINALLY, FOLD THE WINGS DOWN. (I FIND THAT HALFWAY IS BEST)**

8.

## NEXT...

# THE 'SUPERDART'... FOR SPEED

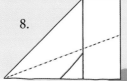

The Superdart is simple, easy, and quick to fold, and a great flyer for speed and distance. So, you won't be surprised to learn that it is the most common type of paper plane ever made. You've probably seen lots of variations. I certainly have. When I take the Bradshaws shows out into the theatres, every seat has a sheet of coloured A4 paper on it so the audience can get right into the mood even before the show begins by making and throwing paper planes. And they do! It's fantastic to watch all the childish grown-ups - and it is usually dads, the kids don't get a chance - having such a great time with something as simple as a sheet of paper. Because it's so quick and easy to do, and because it can fly quite straight, it's a good one for writing messages on to send to someone on the other side of the classroom, or the office. So this is the basic design upon which

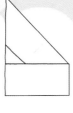

all the other dart-type planes are based and it's perfect for practising your plane-making and chucking skills. A few simple modifications like bending the wing-tips slightly up or down or folding the nose tip in so it's square (and doesn't hurt as much when it hits someone in the ear'ole) can make a difference to the flight. Just experiment.

YOU ARE REALLY UGLY

# HOW TO MAKE 'THE SUPERDART'

1. FOLD A SHEET OF A4 LENGTHWAYS TO GET A CENTRE LINE

2. FOLD ONE CORNER INTO THE CENTRE LINE

3. AND THEN FOLD THE OTHER CORNER IN

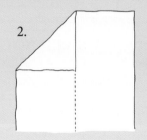

2.

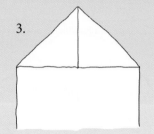

3.

4. NOW FOLD THE CORNERS IN HALF AGAIN

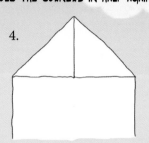

4.

4A. FOLD CORNER 'A' INTO THE MIDDLE

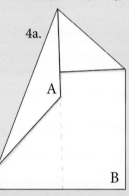

4a.

A

B

4B. THEN CORNER 'B' INTO THE MIDDLE

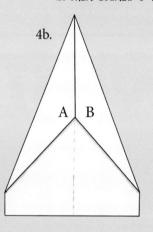

4b.

A   B

5. FOLD THE WINGS DOWN -
THE WIDER THEY ARE,
THE BETTER IT WILL GLIDE

5.

6. TURN THE OUTER WING EDGES UP SLIGHTLY
AND/OR BEND THE ELEVATOR
(THE BACK OF THE WINGS)
EXPERIMENT WITH THESE
TO GET TURNS, CLIMBS AND DIVES

REMEMBER, THIS IS QUITE FAST FLYING
WITH A POINTY NOSE,
SO DON'T AIM IT TOWARDS
YOUR PAL'S FACE!

# THE MARTIAN SPACECRAFT

The 'Martian Spacecraft' is especially designed to fly long distances. By maximizing the wing area on their spacecraft those crafty little Martians achieve really smooth gliding and graceful turning. This bazzin' plane is just made for the high life so, if you can, take this one outside or into a high-ceilinged room and try the 'high throw' technique described on the *Getting The Most From Your Bazzin' Paper Plane* page at the end of the feature.

You can add some Martian-type writing on the wing or along the fusilage, with coloured pens or markers, and make it look really authentic ... e.g.- ZXK323~martianairways (plus a few Martian squiggles). Be sure use shades of green to match the Martian complexion.

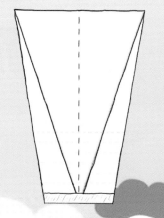

## HOW TO MAKE 'THE MARTIAN SPACECRAFT'

### 1. FOLD YOUR A4-SIZE PAPER LENGTHWAYS TO GET A CENTRE LINE

### 2. FOLD THE BOTTOM TWO CORNERS TO THE CENTRE LINE

2.

### 3. CREASE TO THE TOP CORNERS AS SHOWN

3.

### 4. NOW FOLD THE BOTTOM UP ABOUT 1CM

4.

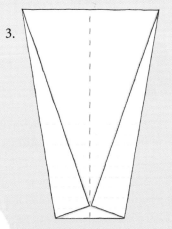

*DOCTOR, DOCTOR, WHAT IS THE BEST THING TO TO DO WITH A LITTLE GREEN MARTIAN? WAIT UNTIL HE'S RIPE.*

# HOW TO MAKE 'THE MARTIAN SPACECRAFT CONT'D'

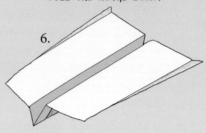

**5.** FOLD UP FROM THE BOTTOM AGAIN ANOTHER 8 OR 9 TIMES. AFTER 6 OR 7 FOLDS YOU WILL NEED TO FLATTEN THE PAPER BY TUCKING IT IN

5.

**6.** NOW FOLD THE PLANE LENGTHWAYS IN HALF AND FOLD THE WINGS DOWN

6.

**8.** BEFORE THROWING IT, MAKE SURE THE WINGTIPS LIE ABOVE THE BODY TO FORM A 'Y' SHAPE (VIEWED FROM THE FRONT)

8.

**7.** FOLD THE WINGS DOWN LEAVING ABOUT 2.5cms (1 INCH) FOR THE BODY. THEN SLIGHTLY TURN UP THE WINGTIPS (EXPERIMENT WITH THE AMOUNT). BEND THE ELEVATORS UP SLIGHTLY FOR BEST FLIGHT

7.

WITH A BIT OF TWEAKING IT CAN FLY LONG DISTANCES AND IT'S GREAT AT STUNTS. IF IT DIVES BEND THE ELEVATORS UP SLIGHTLY. IF IT CLIMBS AND SLOWS BEFORE DIVING, BEND THE ELEVATORS DOWN SLIGHTLY IF IT VEERS TO THE LEFT, BEND THE RUDDER RIGHT IF IT VEERS TO THE RIGHT, BEND THE RUDDER LEFT

# THE HAWK ... LITTLE ACROBAT

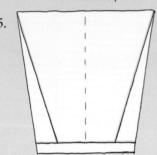

The Hawk has just a little more folding involved but it's well worth that extra bit of effort. And once you've made one (well, maybe two), it's a doddle. With a bit of practice and the right kind of throw it's easy to make it loop-the-loop. And even better, try a bit of experimental wing-tip tweaking and it will be swooping and swerving all over the place. I like to make these with newspaper cut to A4 size. It looks really good - mind you, I love the smell of fish and chips. Anyway, put your mark on it by making it with coloured paper, or felt-tip your name on it so no-one can nick it, cos they will!

# HOW TO MAKE 'THE HAWK'

## PLANES

**1. FOLD ONE CORNER ACROSS TO THE OTHER SIDE TO MAKE A RIGHT ANGLE TRIANGLE. THEN CREASE IT**

1.

1A.

**2. FOLD THE BOTTOM STRIP UP. CREASE IT AND CUT OR TEAR IT OFF NEATLY. THIS WILL FORM THE TAIL**

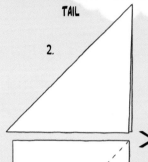

2.

**3. OPEN UP YOUR SHEET OF PAPER AGAIN ...**

3.

**... AND FOLD THE TOP RIGHT HAND CORNER ACROSS TO THE OPPOSITE CORNER. CREASE IT**

3A.

**4. OPEN UP THE SHEET OF PAPER AGAIN. THE CREASES NOW FORM A BIG 'X'**

4.

**5. THIS IS THE TRICKY BIT: TAKE HOLD OF TWO OPPOSITE CORNERS. PUSH THEM TOWARDS EACH OTHER MANOEVERING THEM TO FORM A TRIANGLE. THEY SHOULD LOOK LIKE DOUBLE WINGS**

**6. FOLD TWO CORNERS INTO THE MIDDLE**

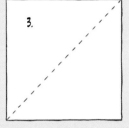

6.

A   B

**7. FOLD THESE TWO CRNERS INTO THE MIDDLE AGAIN**

7.

A B

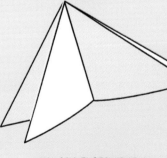

**8. NOW THE TAIL. FOLD IT LENGTHWAYS AND TURN THE CORNERS IN AT ONE END TO FORM A POINT. INSERT IT INTO THE WING SECTION AND FOLD THE FRONT OVER TO HOLD IT**

**9. FOLD THE PLANE UPWARDS ALONG IT'S LENGTH & FOLD EACH WING DOWN SLIGHTLY**

8.

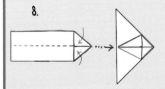
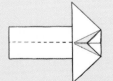

9.

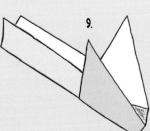

**YOU CAN EXPERIMENT BY TURNING ONE OR BOTH OF THE WINGTIPS UP A BIT TO SEE WHAT DIFFERENCE IT MAKES TO THE FLIGHTPATH. TURNING ONE TIP UP WILL CAUSE IT TO TURN**

# GETTING THE MOST FROM YOUR BAZZIN' PAPER PLANE

I MADE A BAZZIN' PAPER PLANE BUT IT GOT STUCK ON OUR COALSHED ROOF! HE-HEE!

## TWEAKS AND FINE-TUNING

After folding your plane, hold it up and look at it from the front. Adjust the wings so that both wing tips are a little above the aeroplane body. The wings should form a 'Y' with the body. Check that the wings are not warped.

←ELEVATOR

Now adjust the 'elevator'. This is the back horizontal edge of the wing or tail. For slow flight and gliding it's best if the 'elevator' is bent slightly up - but only slightly. For fast flight and hard throwing the 'elevator' is best bent slightly down.

Next adjust the 'rudder'. This is the back of the tail. If it veers left, bend the rudder slightly right. If it veers right, bend the rudder slightly left.

RUDDER

## BAZZIN' THROWING TECHNIQUES

Generally, hold the plane with your finger and thumb on the bottom near the front.

**SLOW THROW** ~ This is for slow gliding and works great when you can throw it from an upstairs window or a hill. And it's the best way to test your fine-tuning tweaks too. Hold it just in front of your shoulder and throw it forward and slightly downward, gently but firmly.

**FAST THROW** ~ This is for flying it fast and straight, like a dart, and works best with 'The Superdart' and the 'The Nipper'. Hold it above your shoulder and throw it slightly upwards for longer flights, level for shorter ones.

**HIGH THROW** ~ Obviously this is best done outside or in a room with a high ceiling. The Martian Spacecraft is the long flight champion (well, Mars is quite far away, so it has to be) and it's well-suited to powerful throws. Tweak it first so that with a gentle throw it flies smoothly, turning slowly. Then, when you're ready, lean back and chuck it as hard as you can straight up in the air.

๑ Try landing your plane on a target or table or landing slrip on the floor.

๑ Play 'catch' with a friend (it's tricky for the thrower to get it close enough to the catcher, and it's tricky for the catcher to grab it without crushing it.)

๑ Bank the plane wings slightly one way when you throw it, trying to make it circle back around to you.

๑ Bend the elevators up a little more than usual and throw the plane gently straight up in the air to make it loop-the-loop.

# THE BRADSHAWS in "GOOSED"

Plump up your cushion and settle yourself down with a nice cup of tea and a digestive biscuit. It's storytime. Here's an exerpt from the forthcoming novel.

"Wow, look!"

Immediately, four lads and one girl follow the direction of Billy Bradshaw's mucky fingernail and stare skywards.

"Wow, ducks!"

"Gooses!"

"Geeses!"

"A herd of 'em!"

"One, two, free, four, five, six, seven, eight, nine!.. wow!"

"In a V-shape!"

"That's the boss one at the front"

"Yeh, that's called flying inflammation!"

"Yeh" I knew that!"

"Yeh, I did as well!'

All six kids crane their necks and rotate on the spot to watch the arrow of geese disappearing over the rooftops. With a desperate honk, one more goose appears from over the terraced row opposite.

"Look at that one at the back trying to catch up!"

They spin around and watch it flapping furiously across the patch of sky above the narrow street.

"Hurry up slow coach!"

"Yeh, hurry up slowcoach! Yer rubbish, he-hee!"

"Yeh, you'll be late for your dinner!"

"Yeh, and it's worms and chips!"

The dilatory goose flaps out of view with a final wait-for-me honk, and Billy, Michael, Norman, Stephen, Kevin, and Winifred continue staring up at the old grey eiderdown sky, just in case.

"I bet they're flying south to Hafrica where it's warm," says Billy Bradshaw. "I read it in a book."

"Or it might be Wales," Stephen Bennett offers. "It was dead sunny in Rhyl when mi mam's boyfriend took us there in the school holidays."

"Or Butlins," says Kevin Carey - just for something to say.

Five pairs of eyes look at Kevin, and then at each other, puzzled. They don't realise just how good a guess that was.

In the distance a goose seems to be laughing.

"I wish I had a pet," Billy says to himself.

Stephen breaks the spell. "Right! What shall we play now?"

A confusion of voices shouts out: "Kerby! ... Kick-can! ... Sthkipping! ... Hide and seek! ... Tiggy ball! ... Sthkipping! ... King of the castle ... Knock and run! ... Sthkipping! ... Heading on the wall! ... Sthkipping! ... Statues! ... Slapses!"

Instantly, everyone yells. "Yeh, slapses!"

Well, nearly everyone.

Winifred Dutton tries a final feeble "Sthkipping", but it's lost in the commotion.

"Ooh, is that the time?" Audrey Bradshaw says out loud to herself as she ties a knot in the strand of wool that she's just threaded through the corners of some torn newspaper squares. It's only a thought, not a question, so she isn't expecting an answer. She gets one anyway, as a voice shouts from a distance.

"That depends, my sweet little hair-shirt…

*Thud!*

"It might be the time, if you're looking at the clock…

*Thud!*

"But on the other hand, if you're looking in the bread bin…

*Thud!*

"It's probably a loaf."

"I wasn't talking to you, Mister Clever Richard!" Audrey shouts over her shoulder in the general direction of the parlour door. She stands up from the table, pushing the chair out with backs of her legs, and says, quietly to herself this time, but with a bit of an edge, "So you can just keep your sarcasticness to yourself … Hm!" Audrey has found that having the last word now and then makes her feel better, even if she is the only one who hears it. And Audrey really hates arguing. Unfortunately, Alf really enjoys it.

Audrey automatically plumps up the cushion she's been sat on, puts it nice and neat and square on the chair, then pushes the chair back under the table where it belongs; something she always seems to be telling Billy to do. Then she picks up the wool and the darning needle and puts them into the big Oxo tin with the other mending stuff. She presses the lid down on the tin but, because it's so full, one corner of it sits up, cock-eyed. With one hand on the top and the other underneath, she carefully carries it over to the big cupboard in the recess next to the chimney breast, reaches up, and puts it in its place on the second shelf. She puts her Mrs Beaton's Cookery book on the top to keep the lid down.

She pauses as she starts to close the cupboard, and looks back over her shoulder. The *Thud! Thud! Thud!* tells her that Alf is still on the other side of the door. Good! Audrey reaches up and takes her Mrs Beaton's Cookery Book back down from on top of the tin, opens it in the middle and takes out a folded card. On the front of the folded card the words "Christmas Club" are printed with some little holly-shapes either side. She opens the card and looks at the list of entries that are written inside in old Mr Bonsall's neatly sloped handwriting. Her Christmas money. It doesn't amount to a fortune - not even enough to buy dinner for one yet - but it's her little secret and she's proud of herself. It isn't easy saving anything out of her housekeeping. And having saved some, it isn't easy keeping it away from Alf's prying eyes and his sticky fingers. There's a little brown enveloped stapled to the inside of the card. After another quick look over her shoulder, she takes some coins from her pinny pocket and drops them into the envclope, quickly folds the envelope flap over and closes the card. Then stroking it affectionately she puts it back into the cupboard.

On the other side of the window, Fleabag the cat sits on the outside lavatory roof. He pauses with one leg stuck up in the air, looks up and stares pleasantly through the window at

Audrey, as if returning her smile (maybe he is), and then gets back down to business.

Billy Bradshaw isn't speaking: a rare event. Even more rare: he isn't thinking about a pet. Unbelievable, eh? But, at this moment he has bigger fish to fry. One of life's big challenges is facing him and challenges don't come much bigger than this for a seven-nearly-eight year old. The challenge is a game of slapses with Norman Giraffe Hinchcliffe.

Billy is seven-nearly-eight. He decided to be nearly eight soon after he was seven in the vain hope that he might be allowed certain privileges, like playing out longer, going to bed later, and being considered old enough to look after a pet. And anyway, birthdays are just about presents and balloons and jelly and cake, aren't they? So once the presents are broken or boring and the balloons are popped or soggy and the jelly and cake is scoffed or trodden into the carpet then it's time to look forward to the next birthday. Of course, it goes without saying that the Tooth Fairy and Father Christmas will remain unaffected.

Billy is desperate for a pet. All his pals have got pets so, he thinks, "it's not fair!" If he could choose (and he lives in hope), he would choose a budgie. In the meantime though, he isn't fussy. Offer him something small, little or tidgy, feathered, finned or furry, two legs, four legs, or eight legs, and he'll take it - and possibly with some of your fingers as well.

As a matter of fact, three legs would be okay too. For instance, Billy's pal Kevin Carey has got a dog named Manx. Manx has only got three legs but Kevin doesn't mind. Understandably, it struggles a bit keeping its balance while doing the sit-up-and-beg trick, and it can only scratch behind one ear, but it's still worth having. In some ways it's even better than having a dog with a full set. Like when Manx falls over because he's speeding round a corner a bit too fast. That's dead funny. So it's worth it. Fully-legged dogs don't do that. And, just like a fully-legged dog, Manx can still drag its bottom along the floor with its eyes all slitty.

The kids have piled into their secret den in the bombed houses, a few streets away: out of sight but still within hearing distance of a shouting mother (even with their fingers in their ears they would probably still be able to hear Winifred Dutton's mother - rumour has it that her voice was responsible for the crack in Bonsall's corner shop window). The bombed houses were never actually 'bombed' but the local kids don't know that - and probably wouldn't want you to tell them, anyway. The most important thing is that the houses look as though they were bombed, so 'bombed houses' is what they're known as. And, quite rightly, kids don't let trivial things like facts spoil the fun. That will come soon enough.

On a flattish rubble-strewn area, inside the battered walls of a roofless bombed house - where the corporation had once started tidying up and then forgot, Billy Bradshaw and Norman Giraffe Hinchcliffe stand facing each other. The other four members of the Budgie Gang stand around them and compare the backs of their battle-scarred hands. Red hands are worn like purple hearts. The redder, the braver.

A gamma ray of sunlight squeezes through a sniper's peephole in the wall and tension mingled with brick dust floats in the air. In the near distance a shunting engine clanks and rattles: it's probably hooking up to a trainload of waggons full of space troopers and munitions before transporting them to the nearby rocket base where they will be launched skyward at a million miles an hour towards the earthbound Mars attack fleet. Here, in the arena of champions (that's what it is today, anyway), another life or death scenario is being played out. The final battle of the slapses competition is about to begin.

The backs of Billy's hands are already stingy pink from the semi-final with Michael Morris. Michael had got him with a few jammy smacks when his nose was itching and he wasn't allowed to scratch it, and it's hard to think of anything else when your nose is itching. It was worth the pain though, and his hands aren't hurting so much any more. After some serious face pulling, and a bout of oohing and ouching and blowing and licking, the original hot red stinginess has subsided to a warm pink stinginess. And beating Michael was just like rubbing a dock leaf on a nettle sting. He landed some belters. Especially the last one where he *accidentally* curled his fingers so that his nails dug into

the back of Michael's hand and made it bleed. A tear was observed in Michael's eye and he was disqualified for crying. It wasn't just Billy that saw it; some of the others saw it too. And Michael's plea of "I've just got something in my eye, that's all!" just didn't wash. Nobody but Winifred Dutton believed him and she doesn't count anyway because, as boys aren't allowed to hit girls (that's the excuse anyway), she isn't allowed to join in a game like slapses.

It's easy to feel sorry for poor Michael. 'Aw, poor Michael!' is how all the mothers refer to him when they see him lurking on the edge of things, standing just out of it all, on the touchline of life's big football pitch, all bundled up in his big brother's cast-off clothes that are two sizes too big for him. It's easy to feel sorry for poor Michael as he squints with a skenny one at who-knows-what, while wearing clinic glasses with a pink sticking plaster covering up the other eye.

And it's easy to think, as poor Michael

himself does, that the clinic must have made a mistake when they stuck the pink sticking plaster over his good eye and forced him to look at life through the skenny one. And it's easy to think, as the other kids do, that the eye behind the pink sticking plaster must be even more skenny than the visible skenny one which is stuck in the corner and is always looking at his nose. Yes, it's easy to feel sorry for poor Michael Morris.

Right now though, Billy Bradshaw doesn't. Because as we all know, in slapses there is no room for sentiment.

And so poor defeated Michael is standing all-alone a few feet away, saggy and sniffing and making little puppy whimpers. He blinks down at his glowing red hands and a teardrop lands on one of them. It hisses. He whinges through his nose and a snot bubble appears at his left nostril. He sniffs up and it disappears again.

Nobody notices. After several gruelling knockout rounds it's the slapses final and the focus is on Billy and Norman as they stand facing each other. To be more exact, Norman is facing the approximate place where Billy's head would be if he were a Hinchcliffe. That is, about three feet higher than anybody else's head. Billy is facing a darn in the front of Norman's woolly jumper. It's about chest height and it's a green darn. Norman's jumper is navy blue. The green darn is next to another darn. This one is red – well, what's left of it is. Billy tips his head back and looks up, and then up a bit more, to see Norman's gappy teeth grinning down at him.

Norman was born with a grin on his face. A slate fell from the school roof once and hit him on his head but,

because he was still grinning, the nuns didn't check to see if his head was bleeding. When he got home from school his mother had to cut lumps of hair out to get his school cap off.

Above his permanent daft grin is Norman's nose and Billy can see right up the big nostrils. From below they look like two bird nests. There is definitely something moving about in one of them. A greenfinch, perhaps? "I wish it was a budgie!" Billy thinks. Billy blinks and shakes his head and forces himself not to think about pets. Not easy, but he knows he has to focus on the battle ahead; otherwise his hands will look like school semolina pudding with jam stirred in.

"Right, now consecrate," he tells himself. "Erm, what did mi dad tell me? Oh yeh! If you can't win fair and square, cheat! He-hee!"

Now he can feel a plan forming. First, so as not to show any nerves, he has to grin right back at Norman, but he's nervous and only one side of his mouth goes up. It's more of a smirk than a smile, which isn't a bad thing in these circumstances. And anyway, he senses it probably looks quite hard, so he settles

for that.

Next: crank up the pressure on Norman. "Right!" he thinks and spits into the palms of his hands. He rubs them together like his dad does before tackling any job. This time he knows it really does look dead hard because the surrounding onlookers murmur excitedly and shuffle in a bit closer.

Next: beat Norman in a staring match - like in his comic where the Cisco Kid is having a gunfight with a baddy and he stares him out first, then he kills him. "Okay!" He locks his eyelids open, ready to stare into Norman's eyes. And, as Norman's eyes are a long way up, he leans back, and then back a bit more, and then he overbalances and almost falls over. This move doesn't look dead hard. The crowd sniggers. To cover it, he looks down at the ground as if he's looking for the uneven bit that made him lose his balance. He gives a sulky sideways glare at the smallest lad in the Budgie Gang, little Kevin Carey, who is standing at the front of the crowd. Kevin's smile fades and he blinks and looks away.

Once again Billy locks his eyelids open. He leans back, ever so carefully this time, and stares up in the general direction of Norman's eyes. The wintery sun flares out from behind Norman's head so that, for a confusing split second, his head looks like a giant dandelion clock. Dreamlike, Billy finds himself blowing at it to see what time it is. It puzzles him to see that bits of Norman's head don't fly off when he blows at it. The others gasp in wide-eyed admiration at this awesome demonstration of Billy's fearlessness. He realises what he's just done and stiffens,

expecting a knuckle sandwich, but Norman just looks puzzled, and blinks. The crowd cheers. Advantage Billy Bradshaw.

Let battle commence. Steepling his hands together as he does for morning prayers in school assembly, he moves his finger tips forwards and upwards until they're a couple of inches away from Norman's big outstretched hands.

As everybody knows, the rules of slapses clearly state that the fingertips of the opposing players must first touch each other before either party may deliver a slap. But …

SMACK!

"Yoww! You rotten cheaterer, Norman! I wasn't heven ready then! Yer s'posed to touch fingers first! … Right then, if that's how you want to play…"

It is.

SMACK!

"Yoww!" Billy yelps again.

*(Lots more follows in "Goosed" the novel)*

CATCH THE LIVE SHOW AT A THEATRE NEAR YOU

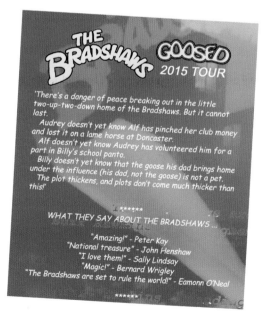

DETAILS AT www.thebradshaws.biz

# BUZZ HAWKINS PRESENTS

## THE BRADSHAWS in "GOOSED"

FLEABAG --->

<--- ALAN PLATT

<--- GOOSEY

<--- HAWKINS

DEBBIE TORR --->

<--- BILLY

<--- DOM COLLINS

**Andrew Vincent** Photography

Pop on to the Andrew vincent website for a gawp at the barrowload of photos from the "2015 The Bradshaws - Goosed" live shows. These photographers can be very unfeeling when it comes to photographing us in unflattering poses, you know!

www.andrewvincentphotography.com

AND NOW, ESPECIALLY FOR NEWLY-RELEASED NUNS, A VERY UNTECHNICAL LOOK AT ONE OF OUR OLDEST GAMES, FIRST PLAYED IN ENGLAND IN THE 16TH CENTURY AND EVOLVING TO BECOME OUR NATIONAL SPORT

# cricket

BRIEFLY, THE AIM IS TO "GO OUT AND STAY IN UNTIL YOU'RE OUT". THE IDEA IS TO THROW THE BALL AT THE BATSMAN'S MIDDLE WICKET AND GET THE BATSMAN OUT. FAILING THIS, TO TRY AND HIT THE THREE STICKS OF WOOD BEHIND HIM. THE BATSMAN HAS TO SEE HOW MANY PADS, BOXES, GLOVES, VISORS, HELMETS AND JUMPERS HE CAN WEAR AND STILL RUN.

IT IS PERMISSABLE FOR THE BATSMAN TO HIT THE BALL UNLESS HE'S PLAYING FOR ENGLAND AGAINST ANY TOURING SIDE. TO SEE THAT THIS RULE IS OBEYED, A WALKING CLOTHES HORSE OR "UMPIRE" IS ASKED TO STAND IN THE FIRING LINE. THE UMPIRE IS THE MOST IMPORTANT MAN ON THE FIELD AS HIS MAIN TASK IS TO DECIDE WHEN THE PLAYERS CAN HAVE THEIR TEA.

CRICKET IS PLAYED ON MANY LEVELS. VILLAGES, TOWNS, COUNTIES AND NATIONS ALL BOAST SIDES. AT COUNTY LEVEL, YORKSHIRE DECIDED SOME TIME AGO TO ALLOW PLAYERS WHO WERE NOT BORN IN THE COUNTY. CLUBS OPPOSED THE CHANGE ON THE GROUNDS THAT IT WOULD WOULD COST THEM A FORTUNE IN BUS FARES.

MANY PLAYERS OF THE GAME HAVE BECOME LEGENDS IN THEIR OWN TEA-TIMES. GRACE, COWDREY, TRUEMAN, BOTHAM ARE ALL NAMES TO BE BOWLED OVER BY. BUT NONE GREATER THAN SID ALCOCK WHO SINGLE-HANDEDLY DEFEATED AN OPPOSING TEAM BY BOWLING A HAND-GRENADE INTO THE PAVILLION. HE WAS NAMED MAN OF THE MATCH BY HIS TEAM AND HIS TEAM RETAINED THE ASHES.

# DON'T WASTE YER MAM'S DRIED PEAS
# MAKE A PEA GUN

ONCE WHEN MI DAD COME 'OME FROM THE PUB A BIT DRUNK, COS THE BEER WAS OFF OR SUMFINK, WELL, HE SAID THAT HE'D MAKE ME A PEA-GUN WHEN HE GOT SUM WOOD. I WAITED ABOUT A MILLION YEARS FOR HIM TO GO AN' GET SUM BUT HE DIDN'T. SO I CADGED SUM OFF MICHAEL MORRIS'S DAD AN' THEN I PESTERED MI DAD 'TIL HE MADE IT FOR ME. MI MAM PESTERED HIM AN' ALL SO HE SOON GIVED IN. THEN, GUESS WHAT? HE MADE ME ANNUVER KIND OF PEA-GUN LIKE A CROSS-BOW AN' ALL!

HOW TO MAKE A PEA-GUN EASY PEASY ...

ALL YOU NEED IS:

   3 STRONG LASTIC BANDS

   SUM WOOD (HONLY A BIT)

   SUM HARDBOARD OR PLYWOOD (HONLY A BIT AN' ALL)

   SUM LICKLE NAILS OR GLUE

   SUM AMMO (DRIED PEAS ARE BESTEST)

A groove so the pea won't fall off

Put the lickle nails in

An' these over 'ere!

the lastic bands go on 'ere!

PING!

Push this trigga, the lastic band comes luse and.... ow!! Watch what yor pointin' it at!

# SOME LET'S-INFLICT-PAIN-ON-EACH-OTHER & TUCKING-YOUR-FROCK-IN-YOUR-KNICKERS-TYPE GAMES

You jump off the top step on to your invisible horse, slap your bum, and gallop up the street to join your pals for some street games.

If the game isn't *cowboys an' injuns*, you just tie your invisible horse to a drainpipe until it's time for home.

If you're a boy, it will be some intellectually stimulating game like Slapses, Knuckles, Chinese Burns, Dead-legs, Toy Fighting (or real fighting), Kerby, Pitch and Toss, Split The Kipper, or just heading a ball against the wall until you go daft. Or maybe that great lads' favourite known as Weak Horse or Crack-a-back or one of a herd of other names. That's the game(?) where the lad who volunteers (or is volunteered) to be 'on' puts his hands against a wall and bends his back like a horse. Then the all other lads pile on top of him. And, hopefully, they all climb off him again before he dies of suffocation.

If you're a girl, you'll be tucking your frock in your knickers and doing handstands, playing three balls against the wall, skipping with your mother's washing line, Chinese skipping with elastic bands, or some other game - preferably one that allows you to tuck your frock in your knickers.

So, in case you feel inspired to pop outside into the backyard and do a bit of skipping or ball juggling or choosing - who's 'on' or a team or a spare sweet - you'll need some rhymes go with your frock tucking (sorry lads). I've collected loads of these at my live shows from all over the country. Here are some interesting ones ...

TUCKING YOUR FROCK IN YOUR KNICKERS

# SKIPPING RHYMES ...

" Miss Polly had a dolly who was sick, sick, sick
So she called for the doctor to come quick, Quick, quick
The doctor came with his bag and his hat
And he knocked at the door with a rat-a-tat-tat
He looked at the dolly and shook his head
And he said to Miss Polly put her straight to bed
He wrote on a paper for a pill, pill, pill
I`ll be back in the morning with a bill, bill, bill"

" Tarzan in the jungle
Got the belly ache
Went to find the toilet
THRWPP! Too late!"

" Mary had a baby
And she called him Sunny Jim
She put him in the bath tub
To see if he could swim
He drank all the water
He ate all the soap
He died last night
With a bubble in his throat"

" All in together girls,
Never mind the weather girls.
Put your coats and hats on.
Tell your mams you won't be home.
I was born in January, February, March ..."
(the skipper jumps out of the rope on her birthday month)

" Skinny Malinky Longlegs
Big banana feet
Went tae the pictures
An' couldnae find a seat
When the picture started
Skinny Malinky farted
Skinny Malinky Longlegs
Big banana feet"

" Bluebells, cockle shells, eevy ivy over!
(turning the rope only half way, then over on
over to continue)
My mother sent me to the store
And this is what she sent me for:
Salt, Vinegar, Mustard, Pepper!
(The enders turn the rope fast and everyone
counts to see who can skip the longest)"

" Not last night but you know the night before?
24 robbers came knocking at my door,
As I went out (run out of rope)
to let them in (come back into rope)
They knocked me on the head with a bottle of gin!
Spanish lady turn around
Spanish lady touch the ground
Spanish lady do high kicks
Spanish lady show your knicks!"

" Cinderella dressed in yella
Went down town to meet a fella
On the way her girdle busted.
How many people were disgusted?"
(count as the skipper jumps)
OR
" Cinderella dressed in yella
Went upstairs to see her fella
Made a mistake and kissed a snake
How many doctors did it take?"
(count as the skipper jumps)

the sugar bowl, And took it to her tea" (glasgow), Ah'm no hairy mary ah'm ye...

## MORE SKIPPING RHYMES ...

" I had a little bumper car, number 48
I took it round the cor-ner
(here, the person doing the skipping jumps
out of the rope, runs all the way round
the rope and the two people turning it, and
then jumps back in while the singers are
holding the sound ' or")
Then I pull my brakes
Policeman caught me
Put me into jail
How many bottles of Ginger Ale?
Ten, twenty, thirty, forty etc,"
(as the rope is turned faster and faster)

" Bluebells, cockle shells, eevy ivy over!
(turning the rope only half way, then over
on 'over' to continue)
My mother sent me to the store
And this is what she sent me for:
Salt
Vinegar
Mustard
Pepper"
(The enders turn the rope fast while
everyone counts to see who can skip the
longest.)

## A BOUNCING BALL RHYME ...

" One two three O'Laira (leg over)
I saw my Aunty Claira (leg over)
Sittin' on her bum belaira (leg over)
Eating chocolate biscuits (leg over)"

## BALL JUGGLING RHYMES ...

" Mrs White got a fright
In the middle of the night
Halfway up the lamp post

Mrs Brown went to town
With her knickers hanging down
Mrs Red went to bed
In the morning she was dead"

## CHOOSING RHYMES ...

" Tell tale tit
Yer mother can't knit
Yer father can't walk without a walking
stick"

" One two three my mammy caught a flea
She put it the sugar bowl
And had for her tea"

" I think I think I smell a stink
Coming from Y-O-U"

" Ink pink pen and ink
Who made that big bulldog stink
I think it was you"

" One potato two potato three potato four
Five potato six potato seven potato more"
(all lined up with two fists out – the
picker, with one fist, taps each in turn and
on " more" that fist is put behind their back,
and so on ... the last fist is on.

" Eeny meeny miny mo
Sit the baby on the po
When its done wipe its bum
With a piece of chewing gum"

" 1, 2, 3, 4, 5, 6, 7, all good children go to
Heaven
When they die their sins forgiven
1, 2, 3, 4, 5, 6, 7"

" Dic-dic-tation, corporation
How many buses are in one station
Close your eyes and think of a number
1, 2, 3, etc ..."

" Oreye oreye jiggereye jiggereye
Onee onee ompom pony
Allowalla whisker (or weesher) chinese
chunks"

JUMBLE SALE

# BREW TIME ... DRIVE YOURSELF MAD WITH THESE BRAINBUSTERS WHILE YOU SUP YOUR TEA

## BUDGIE MAZE

HELP BILLY FIND THE BUDGIE HIDING ON THE OTHER SIDE OF THE MAZE!

## SODOKAY – 1.2.3

NO, IT ISN'T A SPELLING MISTAKE ... IT'S SUDOKU THAT ONLY GOES UP TO 6. AS WELL AS THE HORIZONTAL & VERTICAL LINES, EACH OF THE SEGMENTS SHOULD ONLY HAVE ONE OF EACH OF 1 2 3 4 5 & 6

## TRIANGLE TEASER

HOW MANY TRIANGLES ARE THERE ... BIG, SMALL, RIGHT UP WAY UP & UPSIDE DOWN?

## FIND THE BITING INSECTS

UPSIDE DOWN ANSWERS

TRIANGLE TEASER:
THERE ARE 48 TRIANGLES
OH YES, THERE ARE ...
COUNT THEM AGAIN

WORDSEARCH (BITING INSECTS):
FLEA, FLY, HORNET, MOSQUITO,
WASP, ANT, TICK, GNAT, MIDGE, BEDBUG

BILLY SAYS:
"ERM, I DID MAKE SOME OF THESE HUP ON MI HOWN WIVOUT NO HELP FROM NOBODY EPSEPT MI DAD AN' MI HUNCLE BUZZ A BIT. I FINKED OF TWO OF THE BITIN' HINSECTS ANYWAY! I COULDN'T COUNT THE TRIANGLES THOUGH!

# TELL AUDREY ALL ABOUT IT

### Audrey Bradshaw's Problem Page

**(After living with Alf all these years I'm qualified to protrude into people's affairs)**

Dear Audrey,
I hope you can help me with my problem. It's my son Johnny. He still believes in the tooth fairy, you see, and try as I might I still can't bring myself to shatter his illusions. I know that I'm living a lie but the look on his face when he finds money under his pillow makes the deceit seem worthwhile. I tried again yesterday but when I looked into his innocent little face I couldn't find the words to tell him. As he drove to work at the dental surgery I cried into my handkerchief. I only have my pension and he seems to have such a lot of teeth. What can I do?

From Desperately Deceitful, Birmingum

Dear Desperately Deceitful,
I know that children can be a problem sometimes, what with ice-creams and that. Mind you, your son sounds like he's got a good job so he probably buys his own ice-cream. Not like our Billy, who only has his spends. I asked Alf what he thought about this (of course I didn't tell him your name), and he says next time you should leave a pineapple under his pillow instead, with a note telling him where to shove it. I can't think where he means!

Dear Audrey,
I'm worried sick about losing my hair. My father was bald at thirty and I'm twenty-nine next birthday. I spend hours checking my pillow and counting the hairs in my brush. Can I do anything to prevent it?

From Michelle B, Wigan, Lancs

Dear Mike,
some of the sexualist men in the world are bald... but I can only think of dead ones like Yul Brynner, Kojak and David Niven. Mind you, I don't think they're dead just because they were bald. I could go on (Alf says I do). Lady sealions fancy men sealions, don't they? And they're bald! By the way Mike, you spell your name funny, don't you? Are you a foreigner?

Dear Audrey,
my problem is my next door neighbour, always peeping from behind her net curtains. She never misses anything in our street. The trouble is that she loves to gossip and I seem to be her favourite subject. When I see her chatting with a neighbour I know she's talking about me and the milkman, the postman, or newspaper lad. It's getting me down. What can I do?
From Worried of Eccles

Dear Worried of Eccles,
there's no smoke without firelighters. Be a bit more crafty like my friend Betty Morris and tell your boyfriends to use the backdoor. Mind you, if your nosey neighbour is listening with a glass on the wall it'll make no difference which door they use cos when the walls are as thin as ours you can hear everything. Of course, I haven't tried it myself. I'm only going off what I've been told.

# AUDREY BRADSHAW

Dear Audrey,
I got married four weeks ago and I'm afraid it's all a bit of a disapointment, especially the other. My husband shows no thought for my feelings and is very demanding. I'm aching all over and I don't know which way to turn. Can you help?
From Dolly H., Preston, Lancs

Dear Dolly,
men are just little boys really. They like to have their own way and they sulk if they don't get it. Your muscles will ache at first but as the weather gets warmer you won't have to fetch as much coal in. Buy your groceries in small amounts, then carrying then won't tire you out as much, will it?
P.S. What is the "other" you mentioned in your letter?

Dear Audrey,
I've only been married four weeks and my wife's already started nagging me. I've tried every trick in the book but I just don't seem to be able to please her. What am I doing wrong?
From G. Haystacks of Preston, Lancs

Dear Mr Haystacks,
just the mere fact that you've written to me about your worries proves that you are a man of compression. Married life is hard at first for a woman, so you could try taking the weight off her for a bit until she gets more used to it. Little things mean a lot to us girls so buy her something thoughtful like a trolley bag or a smaller shovel.

deer mam, wen you av finished doing huvver peeples problems please will you do mine? fanks. Can I av a bugjie?
love from Billy x

TELL AUDREY ALL ABOUT IT...
IF YOU DON'T WANT TO GIVE YOUR NAME YOU CAN JUST BE UNANIMOUS. TRY AS I CAN, I CAN'T BE RESPONSIBLE FOR PEOPLE ACTING ON MY ADVISERIES. PLEASE USE YOUR OWN IGNITION.

Dear Audrey,

when I first got married my wife Mary had a perfect figure. Lately she's put on a lot of weight around the middle. When I commented on this she said she'll be slim again in a few months, but I think it's unlikely with all the pickled herring and banana butties she's been eating lately. The other day I followed her to a clinic of some sort and saw her with a lot of other women, all with big beer bellies too. Could she be a secret drinker? She's often sick in the mornings, as I am when I've had a skinful.

Joe Joiner, Kiddyminster

Dear Joe,

you're not exactly worldy-widely, are you? There could be lots of reasons why your Mary has got tubby, and you can count them on one finger. I'll give you a clue. The same thing happened to me just before I had our Billy and I soon got slim(mer) again. So, trust her women's institution, stop following her about, and decorate the spare bedroom. Ooh men!

YOU'RE PROBLEMS LISTENED TO WITH SYMPATHETICNESS

Dear Audrey,

I have an unusual hobby. Every evening when my other half goes out to the bingo I go up to the spare room and dress up. I've bought some lovely frocks and lingerie which I keep hidden in my toolbox. Although I'm now very good at applying make-up I still have a terrible problem with facial and leg hair. No matter how closely I shave, it still prickles me when I kiss the back of my hand, and I ladder every pair of stockings I put on. Even my wincyette nightie catches on the stubble. I realise this may seem strange but I've no one else to turn to. Please advise.

A.Non., Frockleton, Swopshire

Dear Mrs Non,

it isn't unusual at all as most ladies have to shave their legs a bit. For difficult stubble you should use cold cream instead of shaving soap, but see that you wash the razor out thorough or else your other half will know you've been using it. I know a woman who plucks her top lip hair but then she hasn't got any children, has she? So she's got all day. And I wouldn't recommend that new-fangled electricalosis myself as it sounds dangerous, and anyway we haven't got a plug in the bathroom. In fact we haven't got a bathroom. No, I think your best bet is to change to Blue Gillettes like what I have. My Alf swears by them (mind you, he swears by anything).

If ever you're stuck for an answer to one of life's little problems (or a big one like what I am with Alf) don't forget you can ...

TELL AUDREY ALL ABOUT IT

# ILLUSTRATED GUIDE TO OUR HERITAGE    BATH NIGHT!

OVER 2000 YEARS AGO CLEOPATRA IS SAID TO HAVE BATHED IN ASSES MILK...

WHILST THE ROMANS LIKED TO SHARE THEIR BATHS ...

ELIZABETH 1 BATHED ONCE A MONTH ...

WELL, USUALLY, ANYWAY!

THE VICTORIANS BELIEVED HOT WATER WAS BAD FOR THE BACK SO THEY HAD THE SERVANTS CARRY IT FOR THEM ...

WHILST THE RICH USED PERFUMED OILS THE LOWER CLASSES USED SOAP MADE FROM GOOSE FAT AND WOOD ASH ...

GOOSE FAT FACTORY

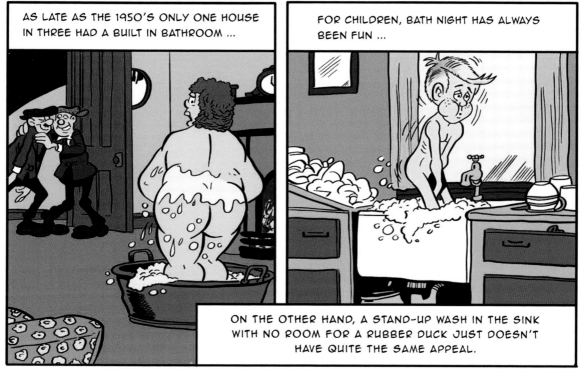

AS LATE AS THE 1950'S ONLY ONE HOUSE IN THREE HAD A BUILT IN BATHROOM ...

FOR CHILDREN, BATH NIGHT HAS ALWAYS BEEN FUN ...

ON THE OTHER HAND, A STAND-UP WASH IN THE SINK WITH NO ROOM FOR A RUBBER DUCK JUST DOESN'T HAVE QUITE THE SAME APPEAL.

# A MATCHSTALK FLIRTER

## HOW TO MAKE YOUR MEASLY SPENDS STRETCH EVEN MORE FURVERER

WHEN MI DAD WAS SHOWIN' ME HOW TO MAKE THIS, WELL, IT DIDN'T LOOK LIKE MUCH. BUT THEN I FLIRTED A MATCH WIV IT AN' IT HIT MI MAM ON HER BOTTOM (HACCIDENKLY ON PURPOSE). AW! YOU KNOW WHAT? SHE FELT IT AN' ALL EVEN THO' SHE WAS WEARIN' HER CORSETS (I FINK). I GOT DONE OFF HER FOR DOIN' THAT COS SHE SAID I MIGHT'VE TOOK HER EYE OUT WIV IT.

MI DAD SAID "THAT'S A FUNNY PLACE TO HAVE AN EYE, AUDREY!" HE-HE-HEE!

### HOW TO MAKE A MATCHSTALK FLIRTER

ALL YOU NEED IS:

TWO ELASTIC BANDS
   TWO HAIRCLIPS OFF YER MAM
      A SQUARE PIECE OF WOOD ABOUT 4" LONG
      AND 1" FICK (10 CM X 2.5 CM X 2.5 CMS)
         OH YEH, SUM MATCHSTALKS
         (I DON'T KNOW WHERE YOU'LL GET THEM FROM)

THEN JUST MAKE IT LIKE IN THE DRAWINGS
   – EASY PEASY!

EDITOR'S NOTE: YOU CAN GET MATCHSTALKS FROM MODEL AND CRAFTWORK SHOPS. OR MAYBE, AS THEY ARE VERY POPULAR IN PRISONS FOR BUILDING SHIPS INSIDE BOTTLES, YOU COULD PERHAPS BREAK INTO ONE AND NICK SOME. - BH

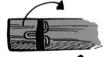

FRONT GRIP PULLED BACK

SIDE VIEW

MATCH LAID ON FRONT HAIRCLIP AND PULLED BACK

BACK HAIRCLIP LIFTS UP TO HOLD MATCH

BACK HAIRCLIP USED AS TRIGGER TO RELEASE MATCH

BILLY SAYS "DON'T AIM IT AT NOBODY ... YOU MIGHT HURT 'EM!"

GET THE KIDS OUT FROM UNDER
YOUR FEET... REVIVE STREET GAMES!

# HIDING & CHASING

## KICK-CAN, KICK-OUT-BALL, TRINNEL & OTHERS

The rules and names varied even street to street but basically the game was played like this:

The can or ball (or kickable object - use your own imagination) was placed in a circle drawn on the ground and someone was selected to boot it as far away as possible. Immediately, everybody tore off and hid, leaving the one *'on'* to bring the can back, replace it in the circle, and then try to find the others.

From then on it was played like Hide & Seek until somebody managed to get to the can first and boot it away again, freeing everybody and putting the poor mug who was *'on'* in a sulk. Sometimes, they would still be on while all the other kids had gone off to Rhyll or some other beauty spot for the summer holidays, having 'forgotten' to mention they were going.

## TIG OR TAG, RALLIVO (OR SIM.), CAT & MOUSE, HIDE & SEEK, JACK JACK SHINE YOUR LIGHT, CHINESE WALL

### TIG *(Tiggy Hit, Tiggy Ball, Tiggy Off The Ground, Tiggy Anything)*

It's best to think of Tig as a 'thing' - like the lurgy, or invisible dog poo, or something equally yuk - that you are keen to give away by touching. So, in *Tiggy Hit* whoever is tigged runs after the others trying to touch them, thereby passing it on, and then running away. *Tiggy Ball* is played with a ball, chucking it at the others to try and hit them and pass tig on. In *Tiggy Off The Ground* you can avoid being tigged by standing on a step or climbing up a lamppost or up on to a window sill. In *Tiggy One Leg* you can't be tigged if you're standing on one leg, and so on for as many versions as creativity allows (*Tiggy With One Finger In Your Ear Whilst Going Sken-eyed* is one I personally wish I'd thought of at the time, because I'm good at crossing my eyes).

HIDING & CHASING

# HIDING & CHASING...CONT'D

**RALLIVO, RALLIO, RELIEVIO** (*spell it how you wish*), and **CAT & MOUSE** are all variants of Tag or Tig and involve a lot of running about, so that lets most adults out.

## JACK JACK SHINE YOUR LIGHT

### Version 1
The one 'on' stands in the middle of the street (the darkest place possible) with a torch (it was usually my dad's bike lamp). They close their eyes and turn around three times. The others have to try to get past without the light shining on them.

### Version 2
This time it's all the others who have a torch. The one 'on' closes his/her eyes while the others run off and hide nearby. The one 'on' then shouts "Jack Jack shine your light!" and the others shine their torches so that they might be chased.

An old and **not-recommended** version was played the same way but, instead of torches, pieces of burning string were swung around their heads. Don't even think about it!

## HIDE & SEEK

Possibly the best known of this sort of game apart from Knock-and-Run, this was and still is sometimes played by parents. The parents' game begins at a certain time on a particular day of the week when any kids in the house are banished to another room and told not to make a sound on fear of death. The parent peeps nervously through the curtains until the one who is 'on', known as the clubman or rentman and often referred to affectonately as 'Raw Knuckles', is spotted in the street. They then dive behind the settee or under a table and stay there until the knocking stops, usually allowing a period of a few minutes to elapse before getting up and resuming normal life. some lucky kids are allowed to hide with the paents. | Often the game is played by the next-door neighbours simultaneously. Their role is to knock on the neighbour's adjoining wall prior to Raw Knuckles reaching their front door.

## WHAT TIME IS IT MISTER WOLF?

This is usually played on either side of the street. The one 'on' is Mister Wolf and he/she stands on one side hiding his face, as in the Hide & Seek (kids' version), while the others line up on the other side. Altogether they call out "What time is it Mister Wolf?". Without looking round he/she shouts out a time, say five o'clock, and the others take five steps towards him/her. At any time Mister Wolf can turn around and try to catch one of them, and they become Mister Wolf. But if anybody manages to reach Mister Wolf and touch or tig him/her, he/she is on again. Despite the name, biting is not allowed.

# THE BRADSHAWS
## "IN THEIR OWN LOONYMATIONS"

Audrey Bradshaw leans over the big pan of hash and prods a potato with a fork. "Mmmm, nearly there", she says to herself. She puts the lid back on and turns the gas down to a low light. As she wipes her hands on her pinny, she becomes aware of an odd click-click-clicking sound. Her first thought is that maybe the long-stopped clock on the mantelpiece has come back from the dead, and she walks over and squints at it. The clock says five-past four as always. It's been pointing at five-past four ever since the little turny winder thing at the back fell off and disappeared down through a gap between the floor boards. If he'd fitted the oil cloth properly right up to the hearth instead of cutting it wrong and leaving a gap for things to disappear down, it wouldn't be saying it was five-past four when it wasn't, she thinks for the umpteenth time. She knows there's no point in actually saying that to him, of course, because he'll only say chuck it out, and she can't chuck her mother's clock out, can she? And, anyway, under it is where she keeps the club book.

Audrey frowns at the clock and points one ear at it. No sound. She picks it up and shakes it near her ear, and it manages just one feeble tock.

Putting it back in its place on top of the club book on the mantelpiece, she emits a frowny 'mmm', turns round and, with her hands on her hips, scans the room.

If it wasn't for the headscarf covering her curlers we'd probably see her ears moving as they try to zone in on the sound. The click-click-clicking seems quite distant. Somewhere over there, in the direction of the stairs.

"Ah!" she shouts suddenly, "I might've known!" And she marches over to the foot of the stairs and shouts up, "Billy! What're you messin' about at up there? What's all that clickin' noise?"

There are only two doors at the top of the narrow staircase and from the other side of one of them comes

an angelic sing-song voice with just a touch too much sweet innocence about it.

"Erm, nuffink, mam!" comes the predictable reply - which makes Audrey wonder why she ever bothers to ask.

"Well, whatever it is you're not doing, you can just stop it now!" The clicking stops.

Seconds earlier, outside in the narrow entry that runs between the back-to-back terraced houses, there is a noise of a different kind. It's the noise of Alf Bradshaw's hobnailed working boots crunching along the cobbles and reverberating off the backyard walls.

A moggy, known affectionately as Fleabag, sitting on top of the coping stones eyes him as only cats can, before noticing the rolled up newspaper in his hand and scarpering, down out of sight into one of the backyards.

As Alf nears his own backyard door something catches his eye. He pauses and looks up. The back bedroom light is flashing on and off.

He reaches under his flat cap to scratch his head. He cocks his head to one-side, frowning, briefly puzzled. But only very briefly. Then the penny drops. "I'll flatten him!" he growls, and stalks in through the backyard door. As he takes the few steps across the small flagged yard, he bellows up at the bedroom window, "Oy!!"

"Right, down 'ere, squirt!"

From upstairs comes a faint Billy-squeak, "Aw!"

"Now!"

"Ooh Alf, don't barge at him!" Audrey pleads, without much hope, as he hangs his coat on the back of the door and joins her at the foot of the stairs.

"Oy! Do you want to see your next birthday?!" he barks upwards.

Three seconds, several bumps and synchronised yelps later, Billy is sitting on the lowest stair having swopped his bottom for his feet and bounced down the last few steps. He stands up rubbing his bum and grinning like a chimpanzee with wind.

"Erm, hiya dad, he-hee!" he says weakly, blinking up into his dad's scowl. "It didn't 'urt."

"Pity!"

Billy gulps.

"Never mind hiya dad. What do you think you're doin' switchin' your bedroom light on an' off? Are you daft? Or is that a daft question?"

"Erm." Billy's eyebrows are up near his hairline now as he blinks some more and tries a chin quiver. It doesn't work. He adds an 'ouch' and another quick rub of his bottom.

This manoevre works on his mam. "It's dangerous playin' with electric, our Billy," Audrey says, gently.

"Erm." Billy turns to her and blinks gratefully.

Then he twists back suddenly as his dad snaps, "Especially my electric! What did you think you were doin'? - Or didn't thinkin' come into it?"

"Erm."

"An' if you say *erm* again, I'll give you summat else worth rubbin' yer backside for."

Another gulp.

"Ooh Alf!"

"Now explain."

And with a deep breath, a swallow, and very very nearly another bottom-threatening *erm*, Billy sets off at full speed.

"I was just betendin' to do the Loonymations by makin' the light go on an' hoff a bit cos mi pal Michael Morris's mam an' dad are takin' 'im on a sharrer[1] to the seaside to see Blackpool Loonymations an' it's not fair cos all mi friends halways go wiv their mams and dads but you never take me to see 'em heven though I'm big now an' I promise I wunt heven mither an' I wunt heven ask for any rock or candy floss or anyfink, so (blink) ..erm - sorry, not erm! (another blink) ..will you? (double blink) ..take me?"

With the help of his eyebrows he gives a quick puppy dog look towards his mam. And even though, in his little heart, he knows it's a waste of a perfectly good puppy dog look, he maintains it when he turns his eyes back towards his dad. "To see the Loonymations? Please?"

He blinks rapidly and forces a poor-little-me smile. His little heart is quite correct. His dad is completely unmoved. Billy quickly looks back to his mam.

Audrey pauses to let it sink in. And then, turning to go across to the stove and stir the hash up before it sticks to the pan, she says over her shoulder, "Mmmm. Yis, I don't see why not, Billy."

Alf groans and slumps his shoulders.

Billy beams. "Wow!" and the little puppy dog look is immediately replaced with that of a demented frog as he bounces up and down. "Yeh! We're goin' to the seaside! We're goin' to the seaside! We're goin' to the seaside!"

"Audrey! Look what you've started now!" Alf groans.

So there it stands on Blackpool's North Shore: a giant tribute to The Bradshaws. Add that to the BBC Radio Four tribute documentary "Thirty Years Of The Bradshaws" featuring John Henshaw, Peter Kay, Sally Lindsay, Eamonn O'Neal, CP Lee and others (still available on the BBC iPlayer) and 2014 turned out to be a very special year for the family.

During the 2014 Illuminations some 50,000 Guided Tour CDs (tongue firmly in cheek) featuring Alf, Audrey and Billy Bradshaw were handed out to Blackpool visitors for in-car listening. It's full of fun and useless information to help to pass the time while sitting in the car.

The great news for me and the family is that the tableau will be shining again in this year's Blackpool Lights. So, if you get the chance, have a ride over to the Lancashire coast and enjoy one of the most famous iconic sights in British culture. And say hello to the Bradshaws.

THE GUIDED TOUR CD OF THE ILLUMINATIONS WITH ALF, AUDREY & BILLY BRADSHAW

POP ALONG TO SEE THE FABULOUS BLACKPOOL ILLUMINATIONS THIS YEAR AND HAVE A GAWP AT THE GIANT BRADSHAWS TABLEAU ON NORTH SHORE

THE BRADSHAWS TABLEAU ON BLACKPOOL NORTH SHORE

# YOUR LIFE AND LUCK

## BY GIPSY AGNES WOBBLYBOTTOM *T.L.R., C.P.M.

*Tea Leaf Reader, Clothes Peg Manufacturer (prop.)

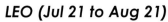

## LEO   VIRGO   LIBRA

### LEO (Jul 21 to Aug 21)

*An urgent change of direction could make all the difference to your personal finances, so dodge behind the sofa quick before the clubman sees you through the window. Interestingly, I see that you may soon be invited out by some very posh people, but don't be tempted to put on airs and graces. Lady Leos: wear your fur coats but resist the temptation to do headstands. Gentlemen Leos: no belching or farting - just for a change. As for romance, you Leos could find yourself in a ticklish situation which will test your moral courage to the full. Oh bugger it, just have a bit and go straight to confession afterwards.*

### VIRGO (Aug 22 to Sep 21)

*Some of you lady Virgos may be having a little trouble with excess weight these days and it's making you tired and out of breath. Either put fatty on a strict diet or switch to single beds. And try to be more efficient in the home. You'll find it will cut down on costs. If you're a lady Virgo you can use the money saved on a nice perm. Remember "A Twink makes men wink". If you're a gentleman Virgo use the money she saves for you to top up her housekeeping, you tight sod! For all Virgos, Venus, the universal goddess of love, has entered your sign and the chance for romance has popped up. Quick, put your teeth back in and change your underwear before it wilts again.*

### LIBRA (Sep 22 to Oct 22)

*The planets are now entering a new aspect and your Libra heart is speaking to you. If you can't hear it, chuck, you've either died or your hearing-aid batteries need warming up by the fire. Libra lads may be asked to help somebody in their career. If it's a lady Aquarian and she's read her horoscope (see Aquarius) be sure to say yes, or wear wooden trousers. Good news, Libra ladies: the adverse aspects of the Sun and Pluto are giving you a sense of well-being and it's hard to wipe the smile from your face. It's either that or you've got a feather down your knickers.*

THE RUNAWAY

THE RUNAWAY

THE RUNAWAY

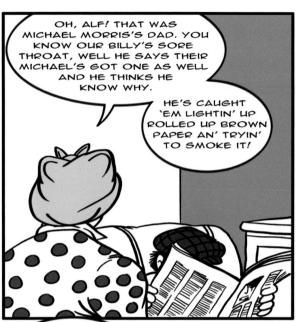

OH, ALF! THAT WAS MICHAEL MORRIS'S DAD. YOU KNOW OUR BILLY'S SORE THROAT, WELL HE SAYS THEIR MICHAEL'S GOT ONE AS WELL AND HE THINKS HE KNOW WHY.

HE'S CAUGHT 'EM LIGHTIN' UP ROLLED UP BROWN PAPER AN' TRYIN' TO SMOKE IT!

BLOODY 'ELL! COME DOWN 'ERE YOU LITTLE SOD!

I'LL GO UPSTAIRS AN' GET 'IM, IT'LL SAVE YOU SHOUTIN'!

I'LL BE DOIN' MORE THAN SHOUT BEFORE I'M DONE! YOU'LL 'AV WORSE THAN A SORE THROAT. I'LL BLOODY TEACH YOU NOT TO SMOKE!

HE'S NOT 'ERE, ALF! HE'S RUN AWAY! OUR BILLY'S GONE!

DON'T BE DAFT, LOOK UNDER THE BED OR IN THE WARDROBE. COME DOWN 'ERE, LAD WHILE I 'IT YER!

THE RUNAWAY

THE RUNAWAY

THE RUNAWAY

*THE END*

119

# WIN FRIENDS AND INFLUENCE PEOPLE
# MAKE A FORTUNE TELLER...

JUST WHEN YOU THOUGHT IT WAS SAFE TO PLAY OUT, SOME GIRL RUNS UP WITH A FORTUNE TELLER. FUN THOUGH!...

**1.**

**1.**

YOUR PAPER NEEDS TO BE SQUARE TO MAKE THIS FORTUNE TELLER SO, FIRST, HERE'S HOW YOU GET A SQUARE FROM AN OBLONG ...

FOLD ONE CORNER ACROSS TO THE OTHER EDGE TO MAKE A TRIANGLE. CREASE IT WELL (THE CREASE LINE WILL BE USEFUL LATER), AND THEN REMOVE THE BOTTOM BIT. OPEN IT UP AND, HEY FABLUARMANDARIS, IT'S SQUARE.

**2.**

**2.**

NEXT FOLD THE OTHER CORNER OVER, CREASE IT FIRMLY AGAIN AND OPEN IT UP. THERE SHOULD NOW BE CROSSED CREASES.

**3.**

**3.**

WE NOW NEED TO MAKE TWO MORE CREASES, HORIZONTALLY AND VERTICALLY. SO, SQUARE ON, FOLD IT IN HALF, FIRST ONE WAY THEN THE OTHER. OPEN IT UP AGAIN AND YOU SHOULD SEE EIGHT SEGMENTS.

**4.**

**4.**

TURN IT ROUND TO A DIAMOND POSITION AND FOLD THE BOTTOM CORNER POINT UP TO THE MIDDLE LINE (I TOLD YOU THE CREASES WOULD COME IN HANDY). NOW REPEAT IT WITH THE OTHER THREE CORNER POINTS (SEE 4A).

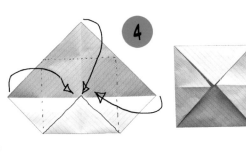

**5.**

**5.**

WHEN YOU'VE DONE THAT, TURN IT OVER SO THAT THE FLAPS ARE FACING DOWNWARDS AND WRITE YOUR FORTUNES IN THE EIGHT SEGMENTS. YOU CAN HAVE SOME FUN WITH THESE!

(HOW TO MAKE YOUR MEASLY SPENDS STRETCH EVEN MORE FURVERER)

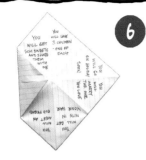

**6**

WE'RE NEARLY THERE NOW ...

6.
FOLD THE LEFT CORNER POINT INTO THE CENTRE.

7.
REPEAT WITH THE OTHER CORNERS.
IT SHOULD LOOK LIKE THIS NOW – – – –>

**7**

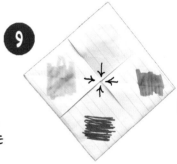

8.
NOW WRITE THE NUMBERS 1 TO 8 ON THE DIFFERENT SEGMENTS.

**8**

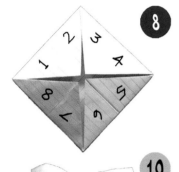

9.
TURN YOUR PAPER OVER AND COLOUR EACH OF THE FOUR CORNERS OF THE FORTUNE TELLER IN A DIFFERENT COLOUR. THEN CAREFULLY LIFT UP THE FLAPS IN THE CENTRE.

**9**

**10**

10.
IN THE LITTLE POCKETS YOU'VE CREATED BY LIFTING THE FLAPS, INSERT THE THUMB AND FOREFINGER OF EACH HAND. YOU MIGHT NEED TO MANOUEVRE IT TO GET THEM IN. NOW HAVE A PRACTICE AT OPENING AND CLOSING IT: TO DO IT ONE WAY, CLOSE AND SEPARATE YOUR FINGERS AND THUMBS; TO DO IT THE OTHER WAY JUST TURN YOUR WRISTS OUT AND THEN IN.

## HERE'S HOW YOU USE YOUR FORTUNE TELLER...

1. WITH YOUR FINGERS INSERTED IN THE FORTUNE TELLER, ASK YOUR FRIEND TO CHOOSE ONE OF THE COLOURS.

2. SPELL OUT THE COLOUR AND, AS YOU SAY EACH LETTER, OPEN AND CLOSE THE FORTUNE TELLER FORWARDS AND SIDEWAYS.

3. NOW ASK THEM TO CHOOSE ONE OF THE FOUR NUMBERS ON THE INSIDE.

4. COUNT OUT THAT NUMBER WHILST OPENING AND CLOSING THE FORTUNE TELLER AGAIN.

5. WHEN YOU'VE FINISHED COUNTING YOU WILL SEE FOUR NUMBERS AGAIN. ASK YOUR FRIEND TO CHOOSE ONE OF THE NUMBERS.

6. OPEN THE FORTUNE TELLER AND THEN READ OUT THE FORTUNE UNDERNEATH THE NUMBER THEY HAVE CHOSEN.

BE CAREFUL WHAT YOU WISH FOR! IF THE FORTUNE TELLER SAYS 'YOU WILL KISS THE NEAREST PERSON TO YOU' AND YOUR FRIEND HAS JUST BEEN EATING CHEESE AND ONION CRISPS, IT MIGHT MAKE YOUR EYES WATER!

# ... AND A PIRATE HAT

One day, little Billy Bradshaw was out playing and he bumped into a bunch of pirates who were struggling to cross the road. He helped them across with the help of his road safety song and then took them home to tea.

So the story goes on the 'B' side of Billy's 7" single "The Easy Peasy Song". It reached no. 109 in the UK singles chart - not bad for a 7-nearly-8 year old!

But, he wouldn't have been able to do any of that if he hadn't been wearing a pirate's hat which he made himself (*'wivout no help from nobody epsept mi dad a bit'*).

Learn how to make one of these, wear it with pride, and, at the very least (depending on your age), you will (1a) look really cool and impress your pals, or (1b) when out shopping with her-who-must-be-shopped-with, get to wait in the car. (2a) Get done off your dad for spoiling his newspaper before he's read it, or (2b) get your own back on your husband for throwing out your shopping catalogue to stop you ordering 'even more stuff you don't need'. (3a) Wear it and make your arch-enemy walk the plank, or (3b) cover up your bald spot. It's as easy as this ...

*A PIECE OF UNFOLDED TABLOID NEWSPAPER IS JUST THE RIGHT SIZE FOR MAKING YOUR PIRATE HAT. BUT IF YOU WANT TO BE POSH, BUY SOME BLACK PAPER (PIRATES HATS ARE USUALLY BLACK, BUT WHATEVER COLOUR FLOATS YOUR BOAT. EITHER WAY, YOU'RE OBVIOUSLY GETTING TOO MUCH SPENDS!).*

1. FOLD IT IN HALF LENGTHWAYS.

2. FOLD IT IN HALF LENGTHWAYS AGAIN. PRESS THE FOLDED EDGE TO CREASE IT.

3. OPEN UP YOUR LAST FOLD. THEN, MAKING SURE A CREASED EDGE IS AT THE TOP, FOLD DOWN THE LEFT-HAND CORNER TO THE CENTRE LINE. DO THE SAME WITH THE OTHER CORNER.

4. FOLD UP THE TOP LAYER OF PAPER TO MEET THE CORNERS A+B. THEN FOLD UP THE SAME AMOUNT AGAIN.

TURN THE PAPER OVER AND DO THE SAME ON THE OTHER SIDE.

5. IF YOU WANT TO PUT A SKULL AND CROSSBONES ON YOUR PIRATE HAT THEN TRACE THE PATTERN BELOW, CUT IT OUT (KIDS, BE CAREFUL) AND STICK IT ON THE THE FRONT. IF NOT, WELL JUST BE A PIRATE WITHOUT ONE THEN. SO NER! OR STICK A GREEN FEATHER IN IT AND BE ROBIN HOOD.

(Just the right size)

... SPEAKING OF NEWSPAPERS (OH YES WE WERE!)

# ILLUSTRATED GUIDE TO OUR HERITAGE — THE BEVVY

MAN HAS ALWAYS NEEDED A PLACE TO RELAX AWAY FROM THE WIFE AND KIDS

THEY FOUND THAT EATING RIPE FRUIT HELPED THEM TO RELAX

AS PUBS DEVELOPED SOCIAL EVENTS BECAME THE NORM

AND EACH AREA HAD ITS OWN FAVOURITE BREW

GNATS

COACHING INNS PROVIDED FOOD
FOR THE WEARY TRAVELLER

PLEASE NOTE: NO HORSES (OR
GNATS) WERE INJURED IN THE
MAKING OF THIS PICTURE

THE VILLAGE INN WAS OFTEN A PLACE TO
TRADE UNWANTED ITEMS

MANY OLD PUBS STILL RETAIN MUCH
OF THEIR OWN CHARM

... WHICH MODERN DESIGNERS
HAVE TRIED TO EMULATE

# YOUR LIFE AND LUCK

## BY GIPSY AGNES WOBBLYBOTTOM *T.L.R., C.P.M.
*Tea Leaf Reader, Clothes Peg Manufacturer (prop.)

# SCORPIO SAGITTARIUS CAPRICORN

### SCORPIO (Oct 23 to Nov 20)

The proximity of Saturn and Uranus together with the recent adverse aspects of the Sun and Pluto have caused a darkening of my crystal ball. Oh no, the electrics gone off. Excuse me while I put a shilling in. It's not my day, is it?! Now where was I? Oh yes. Prepare to meet new people. The uniform should suit you but try to talk in a deep voice - you never know who you might be sharing the cell with. And romance is in the air but girls keep your hand on your ha'penny until you've felt his wallet. Boys take note and be warned: you might well get to hold it but you'll never get to keep it. Just take a picture.

### SAGITTARIUS (Nov 21 to Dec 20)

You could encounter some hazards to your health this month. Look both ways before dodging out of your bit-on-the-side's backdoor. And the answer to all the domestic argy-bargy is very near at hand. Simple. Just turn off your deaf-aid, dear. Financially, no wonder you're feeling confident at the moment with money coming in from all over the place. Beware though. You might catch a chill if you don't start wearing knickers again soon. Generally, making clear decisions and refining certain techniques should save energy. Say 'no' to the wardrobe trick until he's practised on a bolster pillow.

### CAPRICORN (Dec 21 to Jan 19)

Financial pressures are mounting up and you will have to do something positive about it right away. Put your glass eye back in and go and look for work. You're due for a windfall soon but you can't be sure of what it might be or where it might come from. Be prepared: buy an extra bingo ticket and don't walk under a flock of birds. Travel is indicated for Capricornians. Just be natural when you go before the magistrate. The recent Capricornian eclipse makes it important for you to make a fresh start. After the mess you've made of things, you'll really have to pull your finger out, won't you, you dozy old fart!

**\* For a personal reading just send Agnes a photograph of some tea leaves (no tea bags).**

THE LOST CHORD

THE LOST CHORD

THE LOST CHORD

THE LOST CHORD

THE LOST CHORD

Chapped Legs * Will You Fix Mi Roller Skate? * Dad's Black Eye * The Snowball * Volume 02 'In
* Love Letters * Pickles * Mam's Headache & Rickers * Heaster Heggs * Fun At The Fair
* Tupenny All Off * Kites & Woodpeckers * Dirty Washing * Home & Aways * Art For Art Sak
Fluff In The Loft * The Waiting Game * Morecambe Deadline * Keeping Your Head Down * Down The
* The Wood In The Hole * A Touchy Subject * A Woman's Lot * If * A Push Too Far * No Match For Alf
No Laughing Matter * Collecting * Eccles Cakes * Tongue Twisters * Volume 05 'In Their Own
* Just Passing Through * Toy Fighting * After The Fire * Wrap Up * The Last Straw
* Wotsisname? * Open Wide * Puddled * A Baisinful * Taking The Ball In * Beetle
* Holiday Fun * No Flies On Alf * Itchy Bum * Sweet Dreams * Pull Up A Pew * Monop
* Teef & Toytoises * Twinkletoes & The Water Buffalo * To Sleep Or Not To Sleep * Shove Ha'penny * Outdoor
* Dangling Spiders Mysterious Holes * A Good Game * Pumpture Pain & Pot Dogs * More Sweet Dreams * Volu
* Revenge Is Sweet * Sissy Girls * Balaclavas & Bommy Wood * Volume 13 'In Their Own Luc
Penny Wise * Up The Ladder * Life Is A Circus * Shilling In The Meter * First Up Best Dressed
* Whips & Tops & Wobblers * Gentle Persuasion * How Teachers Teach & Teapots Stand * Tricks Of The T
* Battle Royal * On Night Turn * Whistling Another Tune * Stirring Things Up * Crossbar Crisi
Keep On Running * Zorro * Our Gang * Firewood Tuppence A Bundle * Volume 17 'In The
* Broken Hearts & Absent Friends * If The Cap Fits * Bellyaches & Long Grass * Wind-ups & Cock-ups *
* Jujus & Getting The Hump * Confetti Kerfuffle * In At The Deep End * Southport Safari * Sunny Side Of The Street
* When You Die & Ghosts * Glass On The Wall * To Hell With Alf * Coca Dip & Lanry * A New L
* Just Horsing About * Dwarves & Hangovers * Revolutions * Volume 21 'In Their Own Darned
* Alf's Savings Bank * Common Cold * Puppies & Hippos * Slushballs & Ear'oles * Volume 22
* Dressing Up * Woman's Trouble * A Present For Audrey * Just An Ordinary Alf * The Length Of A Piece
* Swollen Clacker * Proper Pooly * Sawdust & Football * Pre-match Entertainment * On Another Planet * Do
* Trolleys & Alleys & POW's * Not Getting The Fever * Something Missing * Handcarts & Happles * Coppers & Co
me 01 'In Their Own Words' * Wot Woz It Like In The Holden Days? * The Monkey With The Funny Coloured Bum * God's
Snowball * Volume 02 'In Their Own Voice' * The Tooth Fairy * Split The Kipper * Taking The Plac
Heggs * Fun At The Fair * Two Balls * Volume 03 'In Their Own Backyard' * Empty Bot
Aways * Art For Art Sake * Press-ups & An' All That * Volume 04 'In Their Own Front Parl
Your Head Down * Down The Entry * Settee Secrets * This Sporting Life * Parlour Games * Volume
Too Far * No Match For Alf * Volume 06 'In Their Own Dog Box 'Ole' * Humpty Dumpty * Penny Black
Volume 07 'In Their Own Kitchenette' * The Mind Boggles * School Baths * Tread Carefully *
Wrap Up * The Last Straw * Volume 08 'In Their Own Dolly Tub' * Early Birds * Horse S
ing The Ball In * Beetle Drive * Over The Top * Volume 09 'In Their Own Thingy' * B
es * Pull Up A Pew * Monopoly Night * Guessing Games * Different Worlds * Volume 10 'In Their
ep * Shove Ha'penny * Outdoor Pursuits * Man's All Heart * Who's For Pudding? * Nuts & Razors * A Little Bit Of Priv
gs * More Sweet Dreams * Volume 12 'In Their Own String Vest' * Jumble Sale * Blowing Your Own Trumpet * B
me 13 'In Their Own Lucky Bag' * Motor Biking * Is It Catching? * Upstairs Downstairs * Wind & Wi
ter * First Up Best Dressed * On The Rack * Volume 14 'In Their Own Footsteps' * Stranded A
ots Stand * Tricks Of The Trade * Cutting Corners * Twenty Questions * Eye To Eye * Rubadub Alf * Vo
Things Up * Crossbar Crisis * Volume 16 'In Their Own Ebb & Flow' * Tea & Sympathy * Legle
dle * Volume 17 'In Their Own Class' * Tin Hats & Hard Times * Crash Diet * Benevolent A
ass * Wind-ups & Cock-ups * Two Shoes Too Big * Back To School * Blue Alf & Cardinal Red * Volume 18
afari * Sunny Side Of The Street * Minding Their Business * The Party's Over * Volume 19 'In Their Own Cobbled Stree
Coca Dip & Lanry * A New Leaf * A Firm Hand * Volume 20 'In Their Own Flat Cap' * Artistic Ten
me 21 'In Their Own Darned Socks' * Out Of Tune * Upright & Bendy * The Lost Chord * Awkward Questions
alls & Ear'oles * Volume 22 'In Their Own Wellybobs' * Happy Days * All Ears * Stick-on Soles *
ary Alf * The Length Of A Piece Of String * Volume 23 'In Their Own Knitted Trunks' * A Little Misunderstan
ment * On Another Planet * Donkeystones & Fishing Nets * Getting The Point * Volume 24 'In Their Own Do